MAINE OYSTERS

Stories of Resilience and Innovation

MW00635714

PERNA
CONTENT

MAINE OYSTERS

Stories of Resilience and Innovation

PERNA
CONTENT

Copyright © 2021 by Perna Content

All rights reserved. No part of this publication may be reproduced without permission from the publisher.

Designed by Blue Anchor Design

Edited by Robert Whitcomb

ISBN: 978-0-578-71562-9

Library of Congress Catalog Card Number 2020911361

Cover Illustration of *Crassostrea virginica* by Aaron Staples
Inset Photo (pg. 1) & B/W Oysters on Ice (pg. 4) by Clifford Tremblay
Panorama (pg. 2-3) Courtesy of Glidden Point Oyster Farms

Printed in China by 1010 Printing International Limited
26/Fl, 625 King's Road
North Point, Hong Kong
Tel: (852) 8226 1010
Fax: (852) 2156 8039

For purchase please contact:

Perna Content
PO Box 736
South Freeport, Maine 04078

www.maineoysterbook.com

CONTENTS

INTRODUCTION

This book tells how highly entrepreneurial and innovative people are developing a virtually new industry by growing, with the help of science, what may well be the world's finest oysters along the gorgeous but challenging Maine Coast. They are doing it even as environmental changes present new hurdles and new opportunities. Then there are such unforeseen events as COVID-19, which has forced big changes in the oyster sales network.

This book is for food lovers, for people drawn to stories about the trials and triumphs of small business, for folks following the challenges of global warming, and for anyone who wants to learn more about the culture and history of one of the world's most storied coasts.

Oysters, of course, have been among the most sought-after food for thousands of years because they are a delicious source of protein, among other reasons, including the idea or hope that they're aphrodisiacs. And while they have usually been harvested in the wild, they have also long been cultivated. Such aquaculture has greatly expanded in recent decades, in Maine and elsewhere.

Oyster farmers come from a wide range of backgrounds – some are from Maine and some "From Away." Some come from generations on Maine fishermen; some are highly educated; some have years of practical experience of working on the water; some are relatively new to this sort of farming. They all share a passion for growing oysters of such quality that they're sought around America. The business tends to evoke growers'

Above: Damariscotta, Sheepscot and Kennebec rivers (NOAA Chart 13293)

Opposite: Winnegance Oyster Farm, on the New Meadows River in West Bath (Jordan Kramer)

rock-ribbed integrity and often surprising ingenuity as they strive to meet the challenges of environmental and economic change. These farmers have a passion for protecting their beautiful coast and a strong desire for personal economic independence, usually coupled with a deep sense of responsibility to local communities, most of which are hundreds of years old.

They want to work on the water even in the face of the effects of fossil-fuel emissions, effects that include the rapid warming of the oceans, sea-level rise, and ocean acidification. They also face new and old diseases and high-end coastal development, with its associated Nimbyism, and considerable public misinformation about what happens when you raise oysters (they actually *clean* the water.) Then, of course, there is bad weather, broken equipment, and other routine problems.

The warming of the Gulf of Maine, nearly the fastest of any salt-water body in the world, has already damaged many traditional fish stocks in the region, and the remaining mainstay – lobsters – is now threatened as the waters warm. The oyster aquaculturists (some of them past or present lobstermen) see their bivalve crop as offering them a way to make a living in places they love, even as other ocean harvests disappear because of climate change, overfishing, and, for some species such as clams, competition from invasive species like green crabs. Oyster aquaculture offers much potential as a growing and *sustainable* source of high-quality protein that actually *improves* the environment that the shellfish grow in. And it's attractive to many animal-rights proponents because shellfish are about as close to vegetables as animals can get.

The oyster farmers in this book display great pluck and the willingness to do hard research, to experiment with new equipment, harvesting methods, locations and hatchery technology, and to take big risks. Again and again, they show the resilience to bounce back from set backs, most of which are caused by forces outside their control.

Some of these growers are taciturn and some are chatty. Most have a sense of humor, albeit some of it mordant. They all want to make this rapidly developing business into a major force in the economy of the Pine Tree State, which could certainly use a dynamic new growth industry, and to set examples of sustainability for the world.

This is a story about inventing and running very unusual small businesses, the rapidly changing natural environment, biology, hydrology and other science, local politics and the culture and sociology of a storied coast. But above all, it's about some of the country's most self-reliant and ingenious entrepreneurs working very hard to bring you delicious food with a romantic and indeed glamorous history.

I originally only wanted to write a narrowly focused work about Maine oysters, inspired by Rowan Jacobsen's beautiful books *The Essential Oyster* and *A Geography of Oysters*. However, as I did research, a wider picture began to emerge.

So it became a story about how people of different backgrounds came together and, over five decades, created a thriving new industry, which now produces what many think are the world's best oysters. The center of the industry is the Damariscotta River, whose clean, nutrient-rich water is ideal for growing shellfish.

The Pine Tree State has many easily accessible, pristine and protected bodies of water that are usually cold but warm when and where they should be for growing oysters. It also has many people with great expertise in aquaculture, including marine biologists and geneticists. Players include the experts at the University of Maine's Darling Marine Center, an incubator for new science, technology, and businesses; the state Department of Marine Resources, which encourages creating new businesses to help Mainers continue to earn a living on the coast; lobstermen and other watermen, some from many generations in the trade with deep practical knowledge, as well as entrepreneurs looking to get into a new industry. All have been smitten with the idea of developing an economically viable culture around the world's most beloved bivalve.

They have overcome countless obstacles and pursued experimentation and innovation with great drive.

In the 1950s the prospect for oysters seemed bleak. The oyster industry's halcyon days in the 19th century, vividly described in Mark Kurlansky's *The Big Oyster*, were long gone. Oysters in such famous sources as the Chesapeake Bay and Long Island Sound were dying off from pollution and disease.

By mid-century, the oyster stocks on the Atlantic Seaboard had crashed and were becoming a fond memory. However, during the 1970s, Rutgers University and the Virginia Institute of Marine Science created a disease-resistant oyster through selective breeding at Rutgers's Haskin Shellfish Research Laboratory in Port Norris, NJ.

In the mid to late 1990s, Bill Mook, of Mook Sea Farm, began introducing that variety into his hatchery in Walpole, Maine on the Damariscotta River.

The central story of the Pine Tree State's oysters begins on the Damariscotta River, which is really mostly an estuary and which for millennia has been a superb source of oysters. The Wabanaki Indians left huge piles (aka "middens") of oyster shells, some as high as 30 feet, that can still be seen on the banks of the Damariscotta. It might be the best environment in which to grow oysters on the planet.

"When the survival of your family is tied to the natural world, sustainability isn't a marketing ploy. It is a lifeline you grasp with both hands."

—Monique Coombs
Maine Coast Fishermen's Association

Following Page: Courtesy of Glidden Point Oyster Farms

WHY MAINE OYSTER AQUACULTURE NOW

The world's population is projected to increase by 2 billion people in the next 30 years -- to 9.7 billion in 2050 from 7.7 billion now, according to a United Nations report. And more and more people have an insatiable hunger for seafood. No wonder that traditional fisheries have been under duress for decades. And so, coastal aquaculture has become an increasingly important way to meet this demand. NOAA Fisheries estimates that the United States imports more than 90 percent of its seafood. NOAA further estimates that about half of this imported seafood is from aquaculture. So there's a compelling case for growing more seafood in the United States. While the U.S. is a minor producer of products from aquaculture, ranked 17th in the world in 2017, it is the leading importer of fish and fishery products. Driven by imports, the U.S. seafood trade deficit grew to $16.8 billion in 2017.

The rapid rise of oyster aquaculture in Maine will have big economic, environmental and cultural benefits, and will provide lessons and inspiration for coastal communities around the world.

The Pine Tree State is at the leading edge of the "Blue Tech" revolution in marine sustainability, and the new version of the "Blue Economy" has become a major player, creating jobs and optimism for those who want to preserve a key part of what makes Maine Maine. Aquaculture of oysters and other shellfish, as well as of salmon and seaweed, helps the state's coastal communities maintain a way of life in which present and future generations can still make a living on the water, in spite of some ominous global environmental trends.

Oyster farmers face daunting economical, political, and regulatory challenges, too. They lack many of the operational advantages of land farmers, such as the latter's relative ease of harvesting, storage and shipping, and they face more vulnerability to some diseases and certain kinds of storms than do land-based crops. Land farmers have access to a wide range of local, state and federal tax and other government incentives and protections that aquaculturists lack. The oyster farmers also face rich and powerful NIMBY forces along some shorelines.

Consider that aquaculturists, unlike land-based agribusinesses, have gotten no federal subsidies, and that while many farms on land create water pollution, and even some air pollution, shellfish farmers *improve* the ecosystems of their working environments. It's not fair. But they press on. Their customers are grateful.

What They Are

The American or Eastern oyster (*Crassostrea virginica*) is a bivalve shellfish native to Maine bays and estuaries that can be found all the way to the Gulf of Mexico.

Opposite: Courtesy of Glidden Point Oyster Farms

Ancient heaps of oyster shells show that oysters were once much more widespread in Maine. Ten-thousand-year-old oyster shells have been recovered from the waters around Mount Desert Island.

For a time after the ice sheet of the last Ice Age receded, much of the Gulf of Maine was a sort of shallow lagoon with warmer water than now. Such conditions allowed temperate-zone fauna, such as oysters, to expand their range.

Then sea levels rose and cold ocean water moved into the Gulf of Maine, restricting oysters to isolated pockets where habitat remained suitable: the upper reaches of such narrow, current-swept estuaries as the Piscataqua, Damariscotta and Sheepscot rivers, where waters could warm enough in the summer for oysters to spawn and survive, and with enough freshwater to keep out most marine predators.

Two thousand to three thousand years ago, the native Wabanaki people harvested large numbers of oysters, leaving behind giant middens of discarded shells. Then something happened, and the oysters began to disappear. Over-harvesting may have been a contributing factor, but some scientists have also speculated that oysters suffered from continuing sea-level rise, which brought in colder water and/or marine predators. And after European colonists arrived, their brickyards, sawmills, forest clearings and other sources of man-made pollution also played a role in reducing oysters' habitat.

Remnant populations survived into the 20th Century. The relic oyster beds provided habitat for other species that became established at the same time: mud crabs, scuds, beach hoppers and other tiny crustaceans. Because the relatively few wild oysters that survived were isolated for so long, they may have evolved unique traits that protected them.

The long history and persistence of oysters in Maine waters inspired attempts to bring them back in the middle of the 20th Century.

Natural Filters

Oysters have an astonishing capacity to clean water with just one of the bivalves capable of filtering up to 50 gallons of water a day.

We know that current oyster populations are a small percentage of what they were historically. We have undermined our coastal waters' capacity to be filtered, and thus cleaned, by shellfish and certain salt-water plants. But we are coming to better understand and quantify the ecological benefits of oyster aquaculture. So we're seeing a new industry of entrepreneurs who are not only providing food but also creating jobs and cleaning coastal waters.

Raising oysters requires no fertilizer, feed, antibiotics or freshwater. Shifting toward eating more aquaculture-raised products, instead of wild-harvested seafood and land-farmed protein, means giving the Earth more of a chance to recover from centuries of resource depletion and pollution.

Ecology

As noted, American, or Eastern, oysters are native to the East and Gulf coasts of the United States.

As filter-feeding bivalve mollusks, oysters grow in periods of warm water (ideally above 70 degrees Fahrenheit for a time in the summer in Maine) and can withstand wide swings in salinity. Oysters feed by filtering algae and other organic matter from the water, and so they take on the characteristics of the places where they live. The taste of oysters varies from body of water to body of water, depending on, among other things, the kind of algae that they eat and the temperature and salinity of the water they live in.

Water quality is obviously one of oyster farmers' biggest concerns. While the filter-feeding oysters help keep the water clear, pollution and harmful algal blooms, including toxic red tide, can shut down oyster-growing areas for months. But if oysters are on the menu, they are safe to eat. The Maine Department of Marine Resources monitors for such toxins as red tide from April through October and for bacteria year-round. And again, shellfish aquaculture is good for the environment, with one oyster filtering up to 50 gallons of water a day.

By removing microscopic plants as they feed, shellfish absorb nitrogen. Nitrogen in shellfish tissue is then in effect removed from the water when oysters are harvested. Further, improved light penetration and reduced nitrogen as a result of oysters' filtering help the growth of eelgrass, a prime habitat of fish and other water life.

Right : Courtesy of Glidden Point Oyster Farms

In and around oyster farms, eelgrass can recover in waters that have not supported sea grasses for decades. Clearly shellfish aquaculture can be an important element of any eelgrass-restoration project.

Recent studies show that shellfish aquaculture can improve species abundance and diversity for juvenile finfish, crabs and other organisms found in healthy coastal ecosystems.

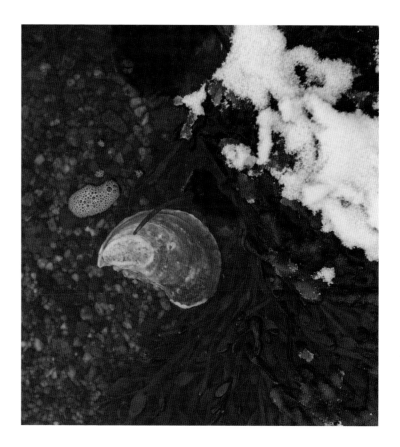

Brief History of Maine Aquaculture

In 1949 the Maine Department of Sea and Shore Fisheries (predecessor of the state Department of Marine Resources) began efforts to re-establish oysters in Maine. Initially, fisheries managers focused on the *Ostrea edulis* -- European or "flat" oysters -- because they were so well known and thus seemed to have high market potential. The state imported them from The Netherlands, screened them for disease and parasites, and planted them in Basin Cove, at Harpswell, Boothbay Harbor and the Taunton River in Franklin. More were introduced to additional Mid-Coast locations in 1954.

In 1972, Herb Hidu, a professor at the University of Maine, began investigating cultivation of oysters in Maine waters, along with Ed Myers and other entrepreneurs. With funding provided by the federal Sea Grant program (in fact, the very first Sea Grant funding in Maine), Hidu developed methods to culture European oysters in the Damariscotta River, next to the University's Darling Marine Center. Experiments were successful -- until the parasite *Bonamia* arrived, in the mid 1980's, and wiped out almost all the European oysters.

So Hidu and the next generation of students continued their research into the 1990's, focusing on *Crassostrea virginica*, usually just called the "American oyster" or "Eastern oyster". Many students earned graduate degrees studying ways to breed oysters to grow faster and be better adapted to Maine's cold waters; some of them went on to start their own aquaculture companies.

Bill Mook, one of the leading pioneers of Maine aquaculture, told me: "In the late '70's, early '80's selective breeding for disease resistance started. The first broodstocks that had resistance were from Rutgers University. The stocks became much better with time and by the early 2000's we were using them regularly. Production of disease-resistant seed really took off when Dr. Standish Allen, a professor and director of the Aquaculture Genetics and Breeding Technology Center at the College of William & Mary's Virginia Institute of Marine Science, got things fired up. We certainly had the best results with those stocks early on. More recently, the Rutgers stocks have really improved, and we now use both."

Above: Two men next to the Whaleback Shell Midden, in Damariscotta, in 1886. The pile of oyster shells was once more than 30 feet high. (maine.gov)

Opposite: Damariscotta River, Damariscotta

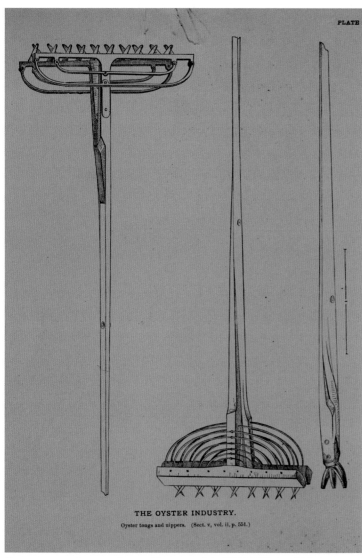

THE OYSTER INDUSTRY.

Oyster tongs and nippers. (Sect. v, vol. ii, p. 551.)

Oyster tongs and oyster nippers (Courtesy of the NOAA National Marine Fisheries Service. NOAA Photo Library)

Mook said that "the modern era of oyster farming in Maine began in 1970, with the hiring of Dr. Hidu at the Darling Marine Center, at the University of Maine in the Department of Oceanography. Dr. Hidu brought the hatchery technology and some of the grow-out technology to Maine. People who are now in their sixties went on to start some of the original oyster farms on the Damariscotta River. The oyster industry wouldn't be here today if it weren't for the hatchery technology developed at the National Marine Fisheries Service's lab in Milford, Conn., where Dr. Hidu previously worked.

"It's very important because with hatcheries you're controlling different life stages of the oyster. In this early process, it starts with the microalgae that we grow to feed the oysters. We select the adult oysters by shape and size to breed to make the oyster babies. We have a whole process to rear larvae. Once they go through a metamorphosis, they become typical bottom-dwelling oysters that you're familiar with. We have different systems to get them up to a size.

"Over the years, hatchery technology has improved …. during the middle part of the 20th Century oysters almost disappeared from the Mid-Atlantic states because of terrible oyster diseases that nearly wiped them out, along with some water-quality issues."

"The grow-out technology has evolved over the years. When I first got into oyster farming, everybody was doing bottom culture. We would grow the seed of the hatchery up a size big enough to plant the oyster on the bottom.

"They are harvested by towing a light drag behind a boat. There are still a lot of oysters coming out of the Damariscotta River off the bottom, as well as in other parts of Maine, but the technology has evolved. Many growers have adopted suspension-culture techniques that rely on periods of air-drying to control biofouling on the oysters and gear.

"And then there's a new technology that we're actually just starting to test out. These are called flip bags or Seapa bags, which are made in Australia. They are mesh tubes or bags holding seed suspended just off the bottom. When the tide goes out, the oysters and bags air-dry, to control fouling. When the tide comes in, they float up and are jostled by wave action, which moves the oysters constantly, improving their shape." The Maine Coast is dramatic, and especially so in the height of its tides. On the U.S. East Coast, the largest tidal range occurs in Maine, with areas near Eastport and Cobscook Bay having daily tidal ranges of 20 feet.

"In the last decade, oyster farming really started to take off," Mook told me. "The demand for oysters has grown steadily right through the last {2007-2009} recession…. It's still growing and there's room for even more per-capita consumption in the U.S."

"Shellfish aquaculture is a huge opportunity for the Maine Coast. Growing oysters, mussels, clams or scallops are businesses that you can get into and the more you do, the better it is for the environment. Aquaculture provides a wonderful boost to the local economy. In a five-mile stretch from below where our hatchery is to above the Route 1 bridge, there are about nine farms providing many jobs and adding millions of dollars to the local economy. There are also spin-off businesses. For example, Damariscotta River Cruises gives tours showing people the oyster farms. Midcoast Kayak takes people up to see the farms. It's really pretty cool to see.

Fishing for oyster with a rake. (University of British Columbia Library)

"What's also exciting is having all these young people getting into the industry. It's not only a huge boost to the local community; it's actually living up to Maine Governor Janet Mills's idea of 'Welcome home.' This new wave of aquaculturists provides brainpower and passion for the Blue Economy. It will lead to innovations that will allow us to adapt and prepare for some pretty big problems that climate change will bring our way."

LION
Refreshment and Oyster Rooms,
JOSEPH C. BUTLER

HAVING taken the stand formerly occupied by John Brown, at the sign of the Big Lantern, has fitted it up in first rate order, and will constantly keep OYSTERS served up in the best manner. Also a variety of other refreshments. Meals furnished at any hour in the day.— Dinners 20 cents. Cuts 6¼ and 12½ cents. Oysters furnished to families in quantities, in any style desired.
Hallowell, Oct. 7, 1847.   4tf

Above: An Oct. 7, 1847 ad in the Maine Cultivator and Hallowell Gazette for the LION Refreshment and Oyster Rooms, in Hallowell, declaring they will constantly keep OYSTERS served in the best manner, and that meals will be furnished any hour of the day.

Opposite: Damariscotta and Gladisfen Postcard

Damariscotta River and "Gladisfen".

HERB HIDU

Aquaculturists who studied or worked with Dr. Hidu include Chris Davis, Carter Newell, Dick Clime, Barbara Scully and Tonie Simmons. Bill Mook studied with Les Watling, a professor of oceanography at the University of Maine. These people were among the sector's original entrepreneurs. They took huge risks based on their confidence, vision and knowledge.

While I was speaking with Dick Clime, co-founder of Dodge Cove and the first oyster-farm leaseholder on the Damariscotta, I learned that Herb Hidu was 93 and still living in Alna, Maine. Dr. Hidu told me by phone that he hadn't talked about Maine aquaculture in 18 years, but he invited me to his house to do so.

I had heard much about Herb Hidu before meeting him. His contribution to oyster aquaculture is legendary.

I met him at his beautiful Federal-style home, built in 1800 on an old coastal stagecoach road. There I met a very lively, charming and fully engaged Dr. Hidu who was eager to share his wisdom and knowledge and was armed with many maps and charts. He became quite serious when I called him "The Father of Maine Aquaculture," a title he quickly disavowed, noting that there are many others who made major contributions in the beginning, such as Ed Myers, Robert Packie, Sam Chapman. David Dean and Mark Richmond.

From 1951 to 1953 Hidu was a paratrooper in the 82nd Airborne, serving during the Korean War but not having to go fight there. With the aid of the GI Bill, he graduated in 1958 from the University of Connecticut with a B.S. in fisheries and forestry management and in 1960 received a master's degree in zoology from Pennsylvania State University, working on the population structure of largemouth bass.

"My first job in 1961-1964 was at the U.S. Bureau of Commercial Fisheries shellfish laboratory. It is now called the Northeast Fisheries Science Center, and is in Milford, Connecticut," he told me. "I worked with Dr. Victor Loosanoff, a very controversial and intense Russian-American scientist. Loosanoff was the son of an Imperial Russian Army officer, and was educated at Russian military academies. At the age of 17, he graduated from the Emperor Alexander I Cadet Corps in Osmk and served four years as an artillery officer in the Russian Army. He escaped the 1917 Bolshevik Revolution, firing a machine-gun from the back of a train, and found his way through Siberia, China and Japan before emigrating to the U.S. West Coast, in 1922. He learned English while working in lumber camps and as a commercial fisherman before enrolling at the University of Washington, in 1924." Herb Hidu recalled, "He was hell bent to recreate the Long Island oyster industry. My job was doing bioassays with shellfish larvae. A bioassay is a measurement of the concentration or potency of a substance by its effect on living cells or tissues. I became very proficient at raising shellfish larvae.

Opposite: The modern era of oyster farming in Maine began in 1970, with the hiring of Dr. Herb Hidu at the Darling Marine Center, part of the University of Maine's Department of Oceanography. (Courtesy of Herb Hidu)

That three-year experience taught me the intricacies of shellfish-hatchery culture. Most importantly, it taught me perseverance."

In 1963 there were massive oyster kills in the Mid-Atlantic states, first in the Delaware Bay and two years later on the Chesapeake Bay, with the MSX (multinucleated sphere X) disease a prime culprit.

Hidu was a Ph.D. candidate at Rutgers in 1964-1967. "I worked with Dr. Harold Haskin. My assignment was to produce disease-resistant oyster stock in the hatchery at Cape May, N.J. The strategy was to compare, experimentally, progeny from oysters that survived the MSX kills with progeny from unexposed populations to see if we could indeed produce an oyster that showed increased resistance. All efforts at the hatchery were focused on developing a disease-resistant oyster stock."
In 1970 the University of Maine hired Hidu to help develop the new federal Sea Grant Aquaculture Program soon after the Sea Grant program was created. The program followed the idea of the Morrill Act of 1862, which was the basis for creating Land Grant

The Darling Marine Center is a full-service marine field station that includes two flowing-water laboratories with resident and visitor lab spaces and state-of-the-art instrumentation. It has a fleet of coastal-research vessels, a variety of oceanographic sampling gear, a scientific diving program and a marine library.

colleges and universities in each state.

David Dean was the director of the Darling Marine Center in 1970 and wrote the report "Culture of Resources in a Cold-Water Marine Environment" as part of the Sea Grant application. Dean's proposal featured developing culture techniques for American oysters, European oysters, scallops and blue mussels. Based on the proposal, the University of Maine entered the Sea Grant Program. David Dean then hired Hidu to help develop the shellfisheries part of that program.

The Darling Marine Center (DMC) was established in 1965, after the industrialist Ira Darling had donated his coastal estate, where he had enjoyed spending summers on the Damariscotta River, to the University of Maine for establishing a marine laboratory.

Today, seven of the nine shellfish farms on the Damariscotta River have ties to the DMC.

Robert Packie

Hidu told me that "I had a student, Robert Packie, something of a wild man, who did significant field work which led to an important paper -- 'The Suitability of Maine Waters for Culturing American and European Oysters'....Packie placed seed oysters at three different temperature regimes on the Damariscotta River. He returned in the fall with a veritable boatload of half-grown oysters demonstrating the potential of the river for oyster culture. This made a believer of me."

Maine Aquaculture Law

Hidu continued: "Right around 1970, the Maine Aquaculture Law was passed. That allowed private persons for the first time to lease suitable areas to raise their own private crops of shellfish, finfish and marine plants. The commissioner at that time was Spencer Apollonio. Maine has a history of a public fishery. A key person, Dana Wallace, was a biologist for the Maine Department of Marine Resources who lived in Harpswell, Maine. As a guest lecturer in my aquaculture course he would explain the 'Free Fishing and Fowling' laws (which started back in the colonial era, when Maine was part of Massachusetts). The colonial laws said that nobody can own anything in the intertidal zone. 'Catch all the finfish and shellfish you want under the law but anyone trying to raise a crop must do so at his own risk.' The concept was under scrutiny with new laws allowing persons to lease areas and theoretically have the ability to protect what they are raising."

Ed Myers

Hidu noted that "Ed Myers was a very influential person in Maine aquaculture. He became our business administrator at the Darling Marine Center. When the state passed the aquaculture law, he obtained aquaculture lease number one. And he did a lot of homework in Europe with blue-mussel culture."

Dick Clime & Gil Jaeger

"Dick Clime got a master's degree at the Darling Marine Center," Hidu told me. "He had an entrepreneurial personality very suitable for aquaculture. He was previously in the Peace Corps in South America. And he was very serious about raising oysters on the Damariscotta River. Gil Jaeger, a lab assistant at the Darling Marine Center, was his partner. Gil and Dick started Dodge Cove Marine Farm in the 1970's. They used three-dimensional Japanese lantern nets.

"They would string the nets out over great lengths. By the time they were finished tending the line, they would have to go back and start again. They did all kinds of innovative things, which ultimately led to bottom culture. They were the first successful oyster farmers in Maine -- that is, they were able to make money."

Left: Ed Myers became aware of mussel aquaculture through the work of Richard Lutz and Herb Hidu at the Darling Marine Center. In 1975, Myers obtained the first Maine aquaculture lease. He would use it to raise mussels in South Bristol. (saltstoryarchive.com)

Opposite: Sonia Clime circa 1980 closing Japanese-made pearl nets on a Dodge Cove Marine Farm work raft on the Damariscotta River. Pearl nets were adapted (as were the lantern nets) from the Japanese practice of growing scallops by suspending them on top of the water column.

Clime recalled, "Our oysters were hung in the deeper water of the Damariscotta River. This reduced the fouling problem we encountered using them in Maine. Scallops can move by swimming, which oysters cannot. So the seed oysters would pile up in a corner of the pearl nets (scallops would spread out) causing uneven, stunted growth. So we changed to a nursery system of floating trays on the water's surface, and later to upwellers for tiny seed, followed by rigid floating bags for the larger seed also deployed at the water's surface. Moving through the progression of nursery systems took about two decades." (Dick Clime)

OYSTER FARMERS TELL THEIR STORIES

Dick Clime, co-founder of Dodge Cove Marine Farm, grew up near Lancaster, Penn. He had never lived or worked by the sea before moving to Maine. After graduating from Cornell with a degree in genetics, he decided to study oceanography at the University of Maine's graduate school. He was one of the first graduate students to work with Herb Hidu at the Darling Center. This gave him his first exposure to oyster aquaculture.

"I thought there was a potential to commercialize oyster raising here,'" he told me. So in 1976 he started his own company, Dodge Cove, the oldest oyster-aquaculture farm still operating on the Damariscotta River.

"Robert Packie did initial experiments growing oysters in the Damariscotta River. This was a very promising place for many reasons. First of all, the tidal exchange, the narrowness of the river, and the sedimentation of the river. The river allowed a lot

of the seawater to warm up. Time for (see below) tidal seawater in the estuary is three days, so the upper estuary becomes a nutrient broth for the phytoplankton. It's a natural culture of phytoplankton to develop there in the summertime."

"Residence time" in this story is the time it takes for tidal currents to completely replace the volume of water within a body of water. Too fast and the water does not warm enough and

Above Left: Packing market-size European oysters (Maine Belons) to ship in cartons to wholesale distributors. Dick Clime explains: "This is me and my partner, Gil Jaeger. My recollection is that the original photo showed five of us packing oysters. We placed them in cardboard trays with cups that apples are packed in. Then eight or so trays were stacked so that the pile would compress the oysters on the underlying trays. The stacks were set into waxed cardboard cartons with fresh rockweed placed on top for moisture preservation. To assist with compression, the cartons were closed and strapped on both ends. European oysters, unlike the American oysters, would tend to open during transit and dry out, reducing shelf life. The compression techniques helped keep the shells sealed and increased shelf life for wholesalers and retailers. We would transport the cartons to a refrigerated truck for direct shipment to New York City, reaching there by the morning after they were pulled from the water." (Dick Clime)

Opposite: Dick Clime (right) and Gil Jaeger (left) spray lantern nets with salt water pumped from the Damariscotta River. "We used the high-pressure spray to remove unwelcome marine invertebrates from the outside and inside of the lantern nets, improving current flow into the nets. That brought the oysters more food (phytoplankton) and speeded growth. With over 1,200 nets in the water, the need for continuous cleaning became too demanding on the crew and ultimately was not scalable for profitability. Therefore, we gave up on suspended culture and after the young oysters had been grown from seed in their nursery, we free-planted (no containers) them in shallow subtidal waters on the bottom for two more seasons. Harvest was then done with a trawl (or "drag" in Maine lingo) when at least 50 percent of the oyster crop was market-size, i.e. , three inches long and with a deep cup. Oysters would be sorted on the work raft, the three-inch and above ones retained for immediate sale, and those too small returned to the water until they grew larger." (Dick Clime)

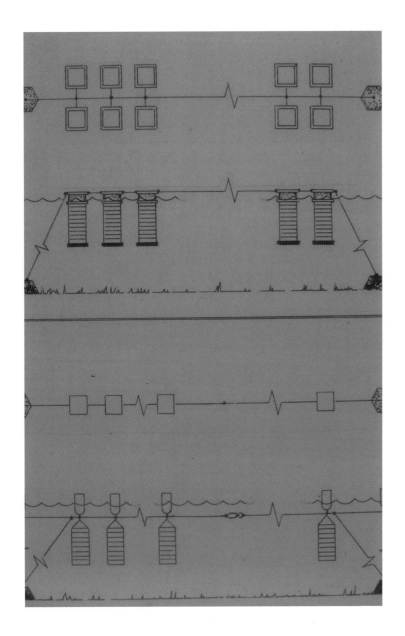

plankton blooms do not concentrate. Too slow and the water can become eutrophic, with low oxygen levels in the summer. The Damariscotta River has an ideal configuration and residence time for seawater to concentrate phytoplankton blooms for oysters. Couple that with the near-perfect salinity in the upper end near the town of Damariscotta, and you get a fast-growing, great-tasting oyster. First you taste the salt and then you get a sweet finish.

Thus the Damariscotta is ideal for growing filter feeders such as oysters. No wonder that this was a place where oysters had thrived for millennia. Clime noted that all these factors "combined, in my mind, to show promise for commercial application."

"Mark Richmond, the (state) marine-aquaculture extension agent, had the very first oyster lease in the state. Mark tried to grow oysters in Blue Hill Bay. There's a salt pond off it. He was not successful there.

"The challenges were acquiring dependable oyster seed," Clime said. "Shortening the grow-out time. Trying to maximize survival

Opposite: In the 1980's early growers experimented with suspension culture, which promised more protection of the crop from predation and the hope that faster growth would result from keeping the oysters in stronger currents away from the bottom mud. At the top are bundles of stacked trays floated under styrofoam blocks attached to a long line moored at each end. This was first used by Maine Coast Oyster Company in the Salt Pond at Blue Hill. Below that, the drawing depicts substituting the stacked trays with Japanese-made lantern nets hung below hollow plastic floats, first used extensively by Dodge Cove Marine Farm in the Damariscotta River. Ultimately, suspension culture was replaced after the first season of the seed nursery with the juvenile oysters scattered on the subtidal mud for one to two years' more growth. This eliminated the labor costs of repeatedly removing heavy fouling from the sides and interiors of the containers, and avoided the capital costs of the suspension equipment for the two- and three-year-old oysters. (Dick Clime)

rates, which was making sure that seed grew enough in the first summer to a size to survive the challenges of the Maine winters. The earlier survival rates of oyster farming were pretty poor. We were lucky to get a survival rate of 20 percent. We lost a lot of oysters. The way you learn is to kill oysters. Early on, until we developed new ways to manage our crop and the timing became evident. Techniques and technology improved."

"In the early '90's, the disease *Bonamia* was affecting our crops of the European oysters. We were growing them successfully in lantern nets throughout the 80's. And we were making money. But then the disease wiped us out. This was a critical time for decisions. We had to decide whether to drop out completely or to change our strategies."

So, Clime said, "The choice we made was to switch to the American oyster, *Crossotrea virginica*."

"We tried a little bit in the Damariscotta in the beginning. And it slowly grew. People were more familiar with the American oyster than with the Belons, European oysters, especially people who were retiring to Maine. Initially…we had to sell wholesale outside the state into metropolitan areas, primarily New York, Boston, Philadelphia, through wholesale distributors, where there was an appreciation for eating Maine Belon oysters on the half shell, and this was a new oyster for customers. We also had to educate buyers as to why the taste of this European oyster was different. We called it the Maine Belon oyster after the French Belon."

"So, there would be a tag connected to it. And the Grand Central Station Oyster Bar (in New York City) was an early adopter and gave us great exposure. They had at that time, maybe still do, the largest menu of oysters possibly in the world. We got a lot of exposure. We never advertised. This was all by word of mouth that we expanded our markets. We attended seafood shows in New York and Boston. We would put up a little booth. Take oysters down there, make up brochures to hand out, and serve people oysters. …So if they requested a taster, we opened a few to provide them with a taste. It was cost-effective in the early days of seafood shows because we were a young company, a small company. We were showing something new and different; that's what people wanted to see."

"The success of Maine oyster farming is due to the increasing predictability and quality of hatchery seed, the adoption of upwellers to maximize the first summer's growth of juvenile seed, the adoption of selective breeding (producing a superior broodstock) to enhance survival and rapid oyster growth, and the continuous improvement of livestock management through observation and experimentation."

"The Damariscotta River is the Napa Valley of shellfish."

—Julie Qiu
International Oyster Sommelier

Bill Mook
Founder of Mook Sea Farm

On my way to Mook Sea Farm, which is in Walpole, I drove through Damariscotta, and its "twin village" of Newcastle. The towns are connected by a bridge over the Damariscotta River. Their connection to each other and the sea is obvious. Both villages are full of grand mansions, historic businesses, and St. Patrick's Catholic Church. Built in 1807, St. Patrick's is the oldest surviving Roman Catholic church building in New England. Many of the

towns' buildings went up during the towns' boom years in shipping and shipbuilding. Shipbuilding began in 1770 and continued until 1920, an impressive 150 years. Over 32 shipyards have been documented, mostly in the upper section of the river, including Great Salt Bay. Square riggers, including clipper ships, and schooners were everyday sights and launches were often community events with great fanfare.

Damariscotta is the center of Maine's oyster aquaculture. The town celebrates oysters with an annual oyster festival, the Pemaquid Oyster Festival, in the fall festival at Schooners Landing. The festival includes food, music and an oyster-shucking competition. The proceeds are donated to the Edward A. Myers Marine Conservation Fund, established in 2003, which sponsors marine education and conservation projects.

In Walpole, also on the Damariscotta River, I met Bill Mook -- a high-energy force. I think that Julie Qiu best describes Bill Mook and Mook Sea Farm in her blog: "No other farm exemplifies both the art and science of oyster farming as well as this one. A scientist, inventor and climate-change activist, founder Bill Mook is an

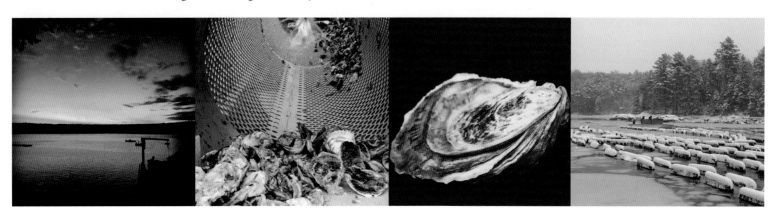

"To be in the oyster farming business, you need to be a problem solver and you have to be pragmatic, but most important, you must be persistent—maybe to a fault"

—Bill Mook

amalgamation of Bill Nye, Jacques Cousteau and Willy Wonka."

One gets the feeling that as Bill speaks he's translating a very complex scientific explanation so that a non-scientist can understand him.

His brain moves very quickly indeed.

As a scientist, inventor, businessman and passionate advocate for addressing climate change, Bill serves on Maine Gov. Janet Mills's Climate Change Council.

Bill recently spoke at a Washington, D.C., meeting with members of Congress to talk about the intersection of aquaculture and climate change. He was there with the Nature Conservancy's Shellfish Growers Climate Coalition. The members, representing all coastal regions, call on congressional leaders to support federal action against global warming, including increased investment in zero-carbon energy and emission reductions for transportation, energy production, and other sources of fossil-fuel emissions.

"In 1998 we came very close to going out of business," Mook said. "There was a septic guy dumping waste into the Damariscotta River about 150 yards from our hatchery intake. We were unable to get a single cohort of larvae to go through metamorphosis for the entire hatchery season. I got tipped off. I started keeping an eye on the guy. I would drive to our property in the middle of the night, turn my headlights off and park at the top of our road and walk down the driveway. I was dressed all in black. I had a small flashlight with a red lens, and I would walk quietly along the shore to his property. I did that every night until I finally caught him draining his tanker truck into the Damariscotta River. I was on the verge of going out

Above Opposite: Mook with Oysters. Below: Courtesy of Mook Sea Farm

"Oyster farmers must have clean water to raise oysters. As an oyster farmer you are a passionate and committed clean-water advocate."

—Bill Mook

of business. I was thinking of how I could sell all the business assets off and not lose my house… We stopped him, but the settlement was minuscule compared to what I actually lost."

Pollution & Environmental Change

"Going back to the original days of oyster aquaculture here in 1988, everybody thought the Damariscotta River was pristine, gorgeous. And it is a gorgeous estuary. In 1998, soon after Smokey McKeen, Carter Newell and Chris Davis got Pemaquid Oyster going, we were all hit with a closure. The closure was caused by elevated fecal-coliform levels in the river, which turned out to be from shoreside homes with overboard discharges.

"We all started working together - Mook Sea Farm, Dodge Cove Marine Farm, and Pemaquid Oyster Farm - to figure out and correct the problem. When the chips are down and we are confronted with a problem or threat that affects us all, we work together to collaborate, even though we are competitors. We teamed up with the Damariscotta River Association, which is now Coastal Rivers, and with Lincoln Academy, the local private high school, and we created a lab. We did water testing, which uncovered a lot of overboard discharge points that were affecting water quality.

"We teamed up with the (state) Department of Marine Resources and Esperanza Stancioff from the Sea Grant Cooperative Extension. A network of water-quality monitoring volunteers were trained by DMR to sample the water. We established sampling stations up and down the estuary and provided the results every year in an annual report. The program was very successful, and through a community effort over a few short years, we cleaned up the river.

"This was a great example of the power of citizen science and community engagement, spurred by a group whose livelihood depends on clean water. The Damariscotta River Tidewater Watch became the model for citizen water-monitoring programs all along the Maine Coast —a fact that gives those of us originally involved a great deal of satisfaction.

"Profound changes in the marine environment are impacting us now and will only get worse. Where we are today is in large measure due to the catastrophes that we have already faced. We believe that the shellfish-culture systems, and their management, developed over many years, will help the shellfish-aquaculture industry adapt to these changes.

"We really focused on improving our technology. When we knew that our water was clean, the question became: How do we use our knowledge and problem-solving skills to create a really dependable process for producing shellfish seed? Since then, we have made a lot of progress towards that goal."

Opposite: Young oysters in hand (CSIRO Marine Research)

Ocean Acidification

Mook said that in 2009 "ocean acidification reared its ugly head. It's a global problem. Carbon dioxide is released into the atmosphere when fossil fuels are burned. About a third of it dissolves into the oceans, forming carbonic acid, making the water more acidic. In nearshore waters there are other factors adding to the problem. Most notable for us is the increased runoff from more frequent and intense rain events. The pH scale runs from 0 to 14, with 7 being neutral, less than 7 acidic, and greater than 7 is basic (or alkaline). … Precipitation and runoff are actually acidic. Unlike seawater, which generally has a pH of greater than 8, rainwater has a pH of less than 6. To make matters worse, especially because of the soils in Maine, freshwater runoff is poorly buffered, meaning that its pH drops faster when acid is added than a solution that is well-buffered.

"In 2009 our larval production was cut in half and we lost hundreds of thousands of dollars of revenue because our hatchery production faltered. Sometimes we would spawn our oysters and they wouldn't develop past the first day or so. More often we would see the larvae develop and feed normally but then all of a sudden, they'd stop feeding.

"2009 was a really wet spring and early summer. Realizing there seemed to be a link between our problems and freshwater run-off, we would try to coax the larvae back with frequent water changes, often timed so we would pump water from the Damariscotta River at high tide. Instead of taking the normal 14 days to go through the larval process, it would sometimes take 21 or even up to 28 days. This was a big monkey wrench in our

Opposite: Winter sunset on the Damariscotta River (Courtesy of Mook Sea Farm)

hatchery production process.

"I'll never forget: It was a cold, miserable day in November. A group of Maine oyster farmers met in Rockland, at the Lighthouse Museum, with two hatchery operators from the West Coast whose larval production had been severely impacted by ocean acidification.

"Allen Barton, of Whiskey Creek Fish Hatchery from Tillamook, Oregon, told us how they figured out what was wrong. After thinking their larvae were dying from a bacterial problem, they discovered what was actually happening. Increased offshore winds were causing upwelling of deep-water. Deep water is much more acidic than the surface water. He described what was happening to their oyster larvae, and we were immediately struck by the similarities."

"We started following advice from Allen Barton and other West Coast hatcheries people, and that was to use sodium carbonate (washing soda) to buffer seawater. Sodium carbonate adds carbonate ions to the water, which increases the pH and makes more calcium carbonate available for the larvae to build their shells. The effects of buffering are pretty amazing, and it's not very expensive. It was like turning a light switch on. … Like clockwork the larvae grew and became ready to metamorphose in 14 days. On top of that, because the larvae were healthier, we started seeing greater yields of post-set juvenile oysters.

"I read the early climate reports and assessments from the federal government and the IPCC (Intergovernmental Panel on Climate Change). They all predicted the increase in intensity and frequency of storms.… We learned the hard way how fresh water is a big driver for ocean acidification in Maine coastal waters, but there was something else that began to concern us - rainfall closures because of bacteria concerns.

"In Maine if two inches of rain falls in a 24-hour period, the Maine Department of Marine Resources closes the affected growing areas to shellfish harvesting. These orders are called Area 500 Maine Coast Flood Closures and they can cover big swathes of the coast. Subsequent to closures, the state conducts water sampling to make sure that bacterial levels are low enough for shellfish to be safely consumed.

"The closures usually last a little under a week to a week. It's not like you can make up those sales. They are lost and as we became more successful at producing market-sized oysters, the closures were increasingly impacting our annual revenue. We started to ask ourselves: How can we deal with that?"

Solution

"Starting in about 2015, we began to plan a new facility to address this problem and provide a number of other benefits. In 2018, our 9,000-square-foot building in Walpole was completed. A key feature is a room that we call the Oyster Inventory Room, or OIR. It contains four separate 26,000-gallon, long and narrow tanks under the floor. A curbed trough runs lengthwise on the floor above each tank, which holds 21 white bins stacked three-high containing mesh trays filled with oysters.

"The room can hold a half a million oysters. It's in completely recirculated seawater or we can pump highly filtered, UV-irradiated exchange water from the Damariscotta River. When big rainfall events threaten, we shut off the inflow of water from the river and operate in full 'recirc' mode. When a rainfall closure occurs, we

continue to ship our oysters.

"Many people ask us if it is possible to grow oysters from egg to market size on land. While we don't believe it would be cost-effective yet, we are beginning to grow seed oysters to a larger size before they are transferred to our leases on the river."

Fermentation Process for Oyster Food Paste

"At Mook Sea Farm, we have developed fermentation technology to grow the microalgae food that we feed the different life stages of oysters. Normally, microalgae cultures are grown using photosynthesis. The microalgae cells absorb light energy to make simple sugar that provides the energy and building blocks for the algal cells to grow and divide. We skip the photosynthesis and provide the cells with sugar. This has to be done in a clean room. It's a very high-tech process. You have to wear a gown; you go in through an air-lock door to get in to work on the cultures. The fermentation process is a huge electrical-energy saver. We're not generating light -- generating light is very expensive -- and we're not having to get rid of the heat generated by the lights. We're able to grow an enormous quantity of microalgae with a very small footprint."

Vibrio

"*Vibrio* are a group of bacteria commonly found in marine waters," Mook told me. "Some species can cause foodborne illnesses, usually from eating undercooked seafood that has been improperly handled. For oysters, the problems can occur in the summer months. *Vibrio* have increased with warming seawater and along with the general increase we are seeing more strains that can be pathogenic to people.

"If you eat an oyster right out of the water in the middle of the summer, no problem. If you take that oyster out of the water and it gets warm for a few hours, the bacteria doubling rates go up and up. Then if you eat the oyster and a pathogenic strain of *Vibrio* has multiplied, you are likely going to get sick. Recognizing this threat to the people eating our oysters and to our businesses, the Damariscotta oyster growers, working with the DMR, developed the Damariscotta River *Vibrio* control plan. The plan provides strict handling and documentation rules that have the force of law and ensure that after oysters are removed from the water for shipment, they are rapidly chilled down. We all abide by the plan and it's been extremely effective in preventing illnesses."

Mook said about climate change: "We should be doom and gloom. Yet wherever there's a problem, there's an opportunity. For example, our ability to sequester oysters indoors during rainfall closures and to continue sales is a business opportunity for us. And we're taking advantage of that. Another example that we will be working on would be using our recirculation facility to reduce the *Vibrio* bacteria in our oysters. We hope someday to have a process that will guarantee that our oysters won't make anybody sick. That's a business opportunity."

"I believe that there's much we can and must do. It's part of our business model to look for opportunities, as we adapt to environmental change, reduce our greenhouse-gas emissions, and work to continually make our business more sustainable…But we also need to push other people to address the root causes, because effective climate action will require an unprecedented global effort. This is what motivated us to work with The Nature Conservancy to start the Shellfish Growers Climate Coalition. The Coalition has grown quickly, and its membership includes farms from every ocean coastline in the continental United States."

"As an oyster farmer, I'm pathologically optimistic"

—Bill Mook

Carter Newell, Chris Davis, & Smokey McKeen
Founders of Pemaquid Oyster Company

Carter Newell graduated from Colby College in 1977. He majored in biology and earned a Watson Fellowship to study snails in Mumbles, Wales, where he took himself and his fiddle; he is an accomplished musician and plays with a Maine country dance band called the Old Grey Goose. In Wales, he spent a year studying snails and visited a marine lab researching cultivation of algae and shrimp. It was there he first learned about Hidu's work in Maine. "I thought this aquaculture was an interesting thing and asked where I could go to study it," he told me. "They sent me to Hidu at the University of Maine."

After five years, he decided to return to Maine and study marine biology. He entered the graduate program at the University of Maine at its flagship campus in Orono. The shellfish-aquaculture program was already well established at the university's Darling Center. Davis, like several other growers, worked on research there under Hidu.

Newell and Davis got together with a third Colby graduate, Jeff "Smokey" McKeen, and formed Pemaquid Oyster, in 1985. McKeen graduated from Colby as a philosophy major. He later earned a graduate degree in folklore from University of Maine and worked as a carpenter. His nickname is a "stage name". At Colby, Smokey took up banjo and mandolin, playing traditional folk music. He has since learned fiddle and button accordion. He formed the band Old Grey Goose with Carter Newell. Many years ago he played a gig where it seemed advisable to use an alias; so one of his bandmates dubbed him Smokey.

"I was friends with Chris and Carter at Colby," McKeen told me. "When they got the idea of starting an oyster farm, they wanted other partners. I joined in. Since I was a carpenter, I built all the equipment: rafts, boats and other things, and then I learned my biology and water skills on the job."

McKeen told me that he had been a landlubber before learning to raise oysters. He said that Ed Myers, who rented wharf space and a mooring to Pemaquid Oyster, often dispensed a lot of "salty advice" to him.

Left: Smokey McKeen (Lauren Hottinger)

Opposite: August Morning on the Damariscotta River Maine (JR P, CC 2.0)

"I sat there and forgot and forgot, until what remained was the river that went by and I who watched. On the river the heat mirages danced with each other and then they danced through each other and then they joined hands and danced around each other. Eventually the watcher joined the river, and there was only one of us. I believe it was the river."

—*Norman Maclean,*
A River Runs Through It

"I'm one of the co-owners of the Pemaquid Oyster Company here at Clark's Cove in Walpole," McKeen told me. "Walpole is a part of South Bristol and this is the old Ed Myers dock - a working waterfront dock. Ed Myers was the first Maine shellfish aquaculturist, starting right here with a mussel farm at Clark's Cove in 1975.

"We have rafts out in the cove that we keep oysters in after harvest before sales. There's also a mussel farm in the cove. There's also a seaweed farm and there are two lobster boats that fish out of this wharf. So it's definitely become a working-waterfront situation.

"We formed Pemaquid Oyster in the winter of '86 and planted our first oysters in the summer of 1986. We thought we would sell our first oysters for 25 cents each. That was a while ago, when 25 cents was worth a lot more than it is now.

"We planted more each year. I forget how many we planted the first year, maybe a couple hundred thousand. Now we buy 2 million seeds a year. We've changed technology over the years. We have various generations of different equipment. We've been harvesting pretty much the same way, either by diving or dragging and now we mostly drag the oysters off the bottom. We grow the oysters as juveniles in floating cages and then plant them on the bottom freely, loosely… They're free-range oysters and they sit on the bottom for a year to a year and a half, and then we harvest them."

McKeen told me that "There aren't any other estuaries in Maine that, like the Damariscotta, have full tidal water 12 miles upstream in a broad river basin. It's a full tide all the way to Damariscotta Village, so it's almost full salinity, and it's very

Carter Newell with the harvest crew, daughter Maise and grandson Elijah. (Courtesy of Pemaquid Oysters)

"I don't know how many times I've heard people say, 'I've been all over the world, I've eaten oysters in Europe, in Asia, oysters in Australia, on the West Coast, but these are the best oysters I ever had."

—Smokey McKeen

shallow upriver. Above the Damariscotta-Newcastle Bridge is a place called Great Salt Bay, a huge tidal basin that acts as a solar collector. So every day in the summer when the tidewater fills Great Salt Bay, a shallow basin, the water there heats up. And then that warm water comes back down and runs across the oyster beds. We get summer water temperatures of almost 75 degrees Fahrenheit. To find a place (on the Maine Coast) with full tide with 75-degree water is pretty rare. Oysters there are eating the phytoplankton from a body of water that's rich in phytoplankton because of the temperatures and the nutrients. And it's very clean water.

"There's a huge market in the Northeast for oysters, especially in New York and Boston and Philadelphia. Northern oysters are better than Southern oysters. I could understand why they might want us to ship to Florida or Georgia or South Carolina. We can get oysters delivered in 24 hours. We lease our growing area from the public, from the state, so we're held to a higher standard about how we operate. And so, we try to be stewards of the river. We pick up the stuff that we see floating by or the stuff that gets pushed up on the beach. We need to keep the water quality that our businesses are dependent on.

"They say an oyster is the taste of the ocean. The same (species of) oyster is grown from northern New Brunswick to the Gulf Coast of Texas. It's the same oyster, but they all taste a little different because they're coming out of different waters.

"Oyster farming is a very sustainable agricultural system. Oysters are feeding on the natural bloom of phytoplankton in the water and are fertilized by nutrients that get washed off the land into the marine environment. With more development on land, more nutrients are being washed into the water. So the extra

phytoplankton that our oysters consume help to keep the marine environment cleaner."

A fine specimen... (Courtesy of Pemaquid Oysters)

"Maine is now known for its oysters and that wasn't the case 32 years ago, when we started."

—Smokey McKeen

Barbara Scully
Founder of Glidden Point Oyster Farms &
Scully Sea Products

After driving down River Road along the very beautiful west side of the Damariscotta River in Edgecomb on a crisp autumn day, I met Barbara Scully at her enterprise, Scully Sea Products, which is just across the river from Mook Sea Farm and next to Dodge Cove Marine Farms. A slender woman in her fifties, she was self-assured and quietly intense. I am certain that this intensity is what let her overcome the many obstacles she faced in building the prestigious Glidden Point Oyster Farms, the company she founded and operated for over 30 years and recently sold.

She is now building a new company, Scully Sea Products, which sells oysters that she grows herself, as well as oysters, clams and lobsters sourced from the area's best watermen. Barbara

told me that after she sold Glidden Point Oyster Farms, she had a non-compete agreement that gave her time to become a long-distance runner, reflect on her role in the oyster industry, and overcome breast cancer. "I found comfort in running, in that it was a super-solitary activity that closely mimicked the diving to harvest oysters that I used to do nearly every day -- just me and my thoughts and listening to myself breathe. I spent over 30 years listening to the sound of my exhaled air bubbles slowly ascending from harvesting oysters at the bottom to the surface."

Barbara Scully grew up in New Jersey and went to the University of New Hampshire at its flagship campus in Durham. She studied at the Shoals Marine Lab, on Appledore Island, in the Isles of Shoals. She told me, "That was a pivotal experience for me as I was somewhat of an outlier, and Shoals was full of people like me - scientists young and old, unafraid to think outside the box and blaze a trail. It was the first place I ever lived in Maine, and the significance of my Appledore Oyster brand."

"My senior project at UNH was a cutting-edge feasibility study of sea-urchin harvesting in the Gulf of Maine. It was keenly relevant and timely for developing fisheries in the 1980s. The urchin-fishery boom soon followed.

"I founded Glidden Point Oyster Farms in 1987, soon after leaving the Shoals Marine Lab. I built a very strong brand with Glidden Point Oyster Farms. I chose the name because of the Glidden Middens, on the Damariscotta, which linked my company to the history of oysters in Maine. Very few people

Above Left: Barbara Scully: "Me with my son, Bennett. He is an engineer in Portland but still comes home to help me on a weekend day if I ask. He misses his former water world and remembers our life fondly." (Bobby Hallinan)

Opposite: Courtesy of Damariscotta Oyster Celebration

were even aware that oysters were a significant part of the Native American diet and culture here. I thought that was a fascinating piece of quiet history. Choosing that brand name allowed me to tie in with Maine's oystering past and bring it into the future.

"People had tried to grow oysters in Maine in the '70s and early '80s and failed. So, I didn't have any examples to go by of what would work. There were no classes or curricula or textbooks. I had to look at what others had done, guess why it didn't work, consider relevant research studies, and formulate a plan of what I thought might work. You trust what you understand about marine ecology and your growing area and try different things. There are so many different variables to consider in oyster aquaculture, and mistakes generally resulted in mortality, so it was a real trial-by-error, seat-of-your pants type of experience.

"As young marine scientists interested in developing Maine oyster aquaculture, the pioneers all knew each other, and knew that we were pursuing the same goal. We bounced ideas off each other from time to time. We knew we were all essentially trying to figure out the same thing: how to grow a Maine oyster-aquaculture industry and make money by making the leap from interesting research project to profitable business. But … we were also extremely independent and very forward-thinking in our own ways.

"Today the original oyster farmers on the Damariscotta River are thought of as a 'group' of pioneers, but we weren't much of a 'group'. We were all so independent-minded. We didn't collaborate a lot because we all had very different ideas of what direction we wanted to pursue. We worked together when we could and when we had to, troubleshooting and problem-solving from time to time, usually in times of crisis, such as pollution abatement, MSX disease or JOD (Juvenile Oyster Disease),

Photo by Barbara Scully

*"That's how it began -- my love for Maine and all its rewards and challenges. I wanted to **live Maine**, not just live **in Maine**."*

—Barbara Scully

48

but we all respected the fact that each of us had different ideas and was choosing slightly different paths. And I do think, in hindsight, that was good. It took us longer as an industry to get where we are today, because we all went in slightly different directions. But we were all successful. And in the long run it made the oyster industry as a whole lot more diverse, and stronger."

She continued, "I mean really, do you expect to fill a room with entrepreneurs and expect them to agree on anything?"

"I recall early meetings, 20 or 30 years ago, looking around at the room, wondering if it was going to end up in an argument, or who would get all prickly first. More recent meetings, I sit in the same room of the same people and think to myself 'I'm proud of us.' I like looking at where we were and what we've all accomplished, as individuals and as a whole. It's an impressive body of work.

"Once investors and manufacturers saw that money could be made in the oyster-aquaculture industry, that infusion of money and pre-made equipment helped the industry grow, but it took decades to get to that point.

"There are many wrong ways to do oyster aquaculture, and mistakes generally result in mortality, but there are also many different ways to successfully grow oysters. And operations do have to vary by site because every local ecosystem is different. Site selection is extremely important. Your site selection dictates what is and is not possible.

"I hope that the newcomers in the industry understand that this industry was grown from outside-the-box thinking, not the cookie-cutter approach. When I look at what's going on with a

Left to right, Aaron Mason, Elliot Barnes, Bennett Scully. The crew was bringing a load of oysters in from the wet-storage raft to be washed and sold. (Chris Ramirez)

lot of the young people in the industry right now, I see a lot of Monkey-See-Monkey-Do. In my opinion that's a risky way to go about things. I don't mean to throw all the new growers in the same bathtub; there are some new operations that are solid… But there are also many operations that are simply buying equipment and putting oysters in it, so it looks like what everybody else is doing. There's a lot more to successful aquaculture than that. A lot of thought should go into each decision that's made in a season. Having sort of a vague, cookie-cutter approach is actually riskier than where we were 30 years ago. Blind trust is a

dangerous approach to aquaculture.

"When your operation is in an 'open system', meaning out in the natural environment (as opposed to a controlled environment, such as a laboratory), you can manage yourself in an environmentally responsible and ecologically sound manner, but still be at risk from the irresponsible behavior of others.

"On one occasion I lost 400,000 seed oysters because someone on a nearby mooring illegally pumped their nasty, oil-filled bilge

Above: Barbara Scully: "My daughter Morgan Scully is carrying the washed oysters up the ramp. In the background, Aaron, Bennett and Elliot wash more oysters with Dobby D. Dog. Seed bags wait in the background to be sieved, thinned out and redeployed. While they are doing these tasks, I am diving to harvest more oysters, which will be placed in the empty green baskets and then put into the wet-storage rafts to be purged. This is a typical, very full day. Morgan now works with severely autistic children, while working on her doctorate in Behavioral Analysis at Western New England College in Massachusetts." (Chris Ramirez)

water adjacent to my lease. Fortunately for the industry, it only affected *my* site. Or if another grower keeps their oysters too crowded, it could create stress and opportunity for disease that would affect the entire watershed. Another example might be a passing boater who might throw some oysters overboard in Maine that traveled with them from the Chesapeake, oblivious to the likelihood that diseases would be spread.

"When the disease MSX hit the Damariscotta River in 2009, I had 10 million oysters on three leases in different stages of growth and 90 percent mortality. It was a devastating financial setback for the Damariscotta River oyster industry as well as to each of us personally. The next three years were harsh. I survived by selling anything I could think of to pay the bills - shrimp, lobsters,

Above: "Sunrise. Getting up early enough to have breakfast, put on your gear, and leave the dock by 4 a.m. is not for everyone, but sunrises and the few hours that you feel as though you have the whole world to yourself are true gifts from the sea. I call my early-morning excursions zen oystering." (Barbara Scully)

clams, wild oysters - while waiting for my first crop of newly bred MSX-resistant oysters to grow.

"The heartbreaking part was that during that period I had to continue to harvest all the leases, spending a tremendous amount of time and energy removing the dead oysters so I could eventually replant healthy disease-resistant seed. On a day of harvesting, instead of coming home with 3,000 oysters to sell, I was yielding a few hundred live oysters and the rest were empty shells.

"I had to somehow keep my head above water for three years until that first-year class of MSX-resistant oysters could grow to market size. It was basically starting over again, and it was overwhelming to think of it all at once. It seemed impossible to overcome. I found that if I could keep my mind focused on smaller segments of the larger problem, and stay in problem-solving mode, I could manage the despair and keep moving forward one day at a time.

"People frequently ask me for historical photos of the sea farm over the last 34 years. I don't have many. I was always working with both hands, not a camera in one. First of all, I didn't have a camera in my phone, and I didn't have a phone in my pocket. I had a landline and in my pocket were a few coins in case I needed to use a pay phone. The days I did manage to remember to bring a camera, my hands were usually wet, salty and dirty and the camera never got used. Regretfully, I don't have many mementos.

"Traditional fisheries have been under duress for decades. The changing climate is changing population distributions. There are historical centers of commerce for certain fisheries, where the infrastructure and fishermen are equipped to harvest a certain species. If that species has moved several hundred or thousand

miles away, then those people have to find something else to do.

"Aquaculture can help supplement traditional fishing communities and buffer the economic impact of declines in natural populations. Fishing communities need to be able to adapt and respond in a fluid way to environmental changes, increasing regulations, and to the cultural changes that follow. Aquaculture is now a significantly important piece of the new face of the working waterfront."

Above: "Starting another harvest dive. Once on bottom I placed market-size oysters in my catch bags by hand, one by one, leaving the smaller ones behind to grow. The water depth varied from 10 to 40 feet, and a typical length of dive for me was 1.5 hours per tank. I usually dove 2 to 3 tanks per day, 3 to 5 days a week." (Chris Ramirez)

ADAPT & DIVERSIFY

Fortunately, the marine biologists were eager to share their knowledge. A lot of fishermen want to diversify, especially given the boom-and-bust nature of fishing. They face climate-change uncertainties, erratic fuel costs, lobster tariffs, ocean acidification (connected to climate change), lobster and other sea-life migration (also linked to climate change), sometimes confusing government regulations and other issues. Thus, many Maine fishermen seek new ways to continue to earn a living on the coast. That now includes oyster aquaculture. Highly skilled Maine fishermen who understand how to efficiently work on the water soon began to learn the science of oyster aquaculture. The Maine Aquaculture Innovation Center, among other groups, began offering courses to teach fishermen how to become oyster farmers so that they, and perhaps their children and grandchildren, can keep earning a living on their state's famously scenic coast.

As the aquaculture industry has grown, so have opportunities for watermen from traditional fisheries to create their own aquaculture enterprises, or to find work applying their commercial-fishing skills to existing aquaculture operations.

"People sometimes ask Carter Newell and me if we're stabbing ourselves in the back by giving away our expertise. We're not afraid of competition. There's a tremendous market for the product. We enjoy teaching, plus we're happy to see acceptance of aquaculture expand, particularly in the traditional fisheries sector. We hope that when our students' cohorts see them up and running and successful, it will help them see aquaculture as a viable alternative."

—Chris Davis
Working Waterfront (Hendrix 1999)

Opposite: Jonathan Tucotte, general manager at Glidden Point Oyster Farms (Courtesy of Glidden Point Oyster Farms)

The Warming of the Gulf of Maine

Gulf of Maine Research Institute, Feb 14, 2018
Dr. Andrew Pershing

"Wherever you look in the global ocean, you're going to find an area that's warming. But places are warming at different rates. And right now, the Gulf of Maine is one of the fastest-warming places in the global ocean. We really started looking carefully at the temperature here in the Gulf of Maine in 2012, which was our ocean heat-wave year. It was the warmest year ever in the Gulf of Maine. What set us off were all of the things that people were bringing into the lab -- black sea bass, blue crabs, seahorses. All of these species that we think of as coming from south of Cape Cod were suddenly showing up on the shores here in Maine. We started looking at temperature records, really focusing on the satellite data that go back to the early 1980s.

"And when you break apart that data, you see that there's a gradual trend that we've had in the Gulf of Maine that's about four times the global average rate of warming. A lot of our warming occurred from 2004 through 2016. We warmed faster than 99 percent of the global ocean. So when people ask me why the Gulf of Maine is warming so fast, well, the short answer is that it's due to manmade global warming and changing ocean currents. And we can think of that really in three steps. So because of manmade global warming we have extra carbon dioxide in the atmosphere, and that means that the Earth is warming, and a lot of that heat is going into the ocean. So ocean areas all over the world are warming, but the Gulf of Maine is warming faster.

"The North Atlantic has a circulation pattern that's driven by cold, dense water that forms in the North Atlantic. Adding a

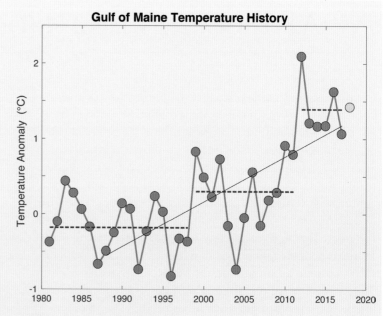

Source: Gulf of Maine Research Institute

"We've spent the last decade identifying warming trends and associated challenges," said Don Perkins, a Maine native who has been at Gulf of Maine Research Institute's helm for almost 25 years. "We'll spend the next decade identifying solutions to some of those challenges and helping coastal communities adapt to a warming future."

—*Don Perkins*
Gulf of Maine Research Institute

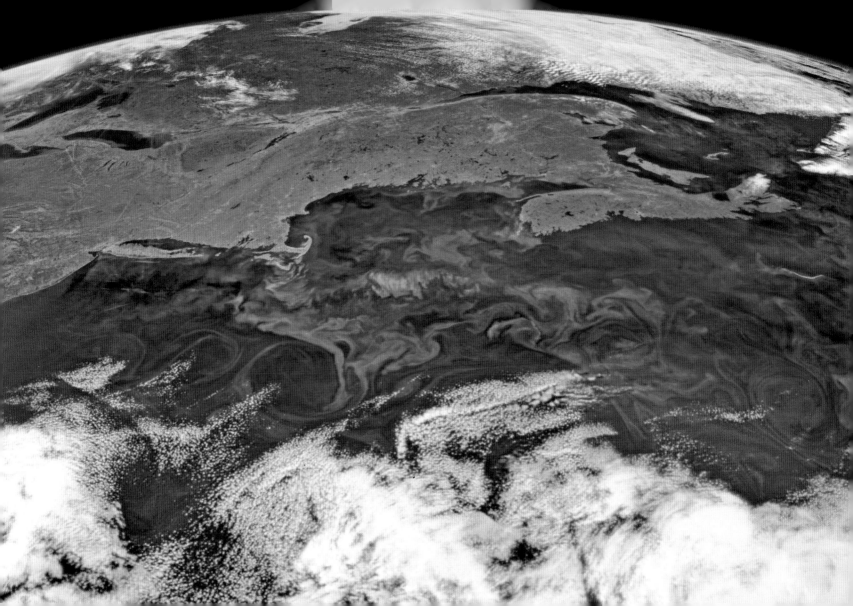

little bit of freshwater due to melting in the Arctic and melting in Greenland messes up that cold sinking water and that changes the whole circulation pattern in the North Atlantic, and the Gulf of Maine is in this really unique part of that global circulation. So, we're right at the boundary between these cold- and warm-water masses or cold and warm currents. And the little bit of warming, the changes in the freshwater, mean that the warm current winds up in the Gulf of Maine, and it's just like a bathtub where you're turning on the cold- or the warm-water tap and we're currently turning the cold-water tap down and the Gulf of Maine warms up really fast."

"We need to change the way we see the world."

—Andrew Pershing
Gulf of Maine Research Institute

Previous: The Gulf of Maine is bounded by Nova Scotia and Cape Cod. The variability of current circulation in the gulf drives many important ecological processes in the region. Modeling ocean circulation is an important tool for understanding and predicting the circulation dynamics in this region. (NASA's Earth Observatory)

Above: Andrew Pershing (Courtesy of Portland Press Herald)

Opposite: Gulf of Maine (NOAA)

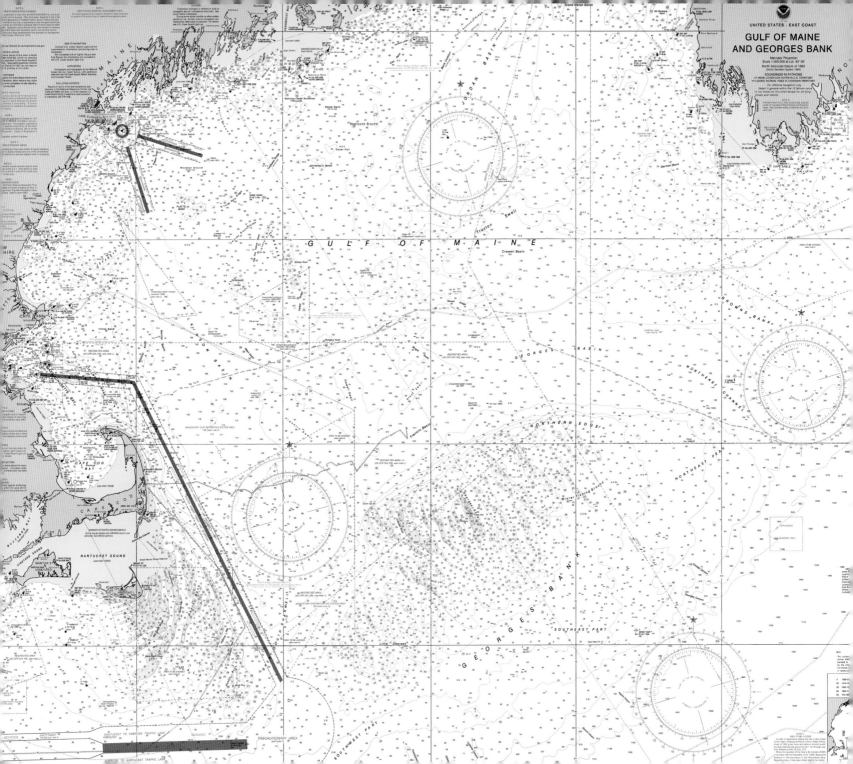

UNITED STATES - EAST COAST

GULF OF MAINE
AND GEORGES BANK

Mercator Projection
Scale 1:500,000 at Lat. 42°00'
North American Datum of 1983
(World Geodetic System 1984)

SOUNDINGS IN FATHOMS
AT MEAN LOWER LOW WATER IN U.S. TERRITORY
AT LOWEST NORMAL TIDES IN CANADIAN TERRITORY

GULF OF MAINE

GEORGES BANK

Eric Horne & Valy Steverlynck
Flying Point Oysters

Eric Horne and his wife, Valy Steverlynck, of Flying Point Oysters, are in Maquoit Sound. They are part of a multi-generational aquaculture fishery that is likely to become more prevalent in Maine. Eric's father, Peter Horne, and his friend Dana Wallace were experimenting in the late '70s and early '80s with quahog aquaculture and oyster aquaculture in the waters in Freeport.

"My brother and I were always in boats and playing around the dock while Dad was working on the mud flats," Eric told me. ''We'd build fires and cook mussels and clams. We grew up with shellfish." He and his brother helped out as they grew older, and Eric also worked at Brewer's Marine, in South Freeport.

Eric went to Brown University, where he majored in international relations. There he met Valy, who had come to the United States from Argentina to study fine arts. After college Eric taught school on Cape Cod, then completed a M.Ed. at Harvard and worked as an education consultant in Boston. Valy completed an M.A. in fine arts at the University of Wisconsin and then went to work as a designer for an architectural firm in Boston.

For several years each summer they returned to help Eric's dad with his oyster farm. Eric and Valy decided that working together oyster farming in Maine was preferable to the rat race in Boston, where they had little time together and faced the unappealing prospect of having to put their children in full-time day care.

They returned to Maine in 2000 and began working in partnership with Eric's father at his Maine Oyster Farms, in Maquoit Bay. They have never regretted the move. They enjoy working outdoors. Valy says being on the water gives her the same feeling of wide-open space she enjoyed growing up on a cattle ranch. They have discovered the truth of a definition of "entrepreneur". Eric once heard: "An entrepreneur is a person who works 24 hours a day for himself to avoid having to work 8 hours a day for someone else." So despite the long hours, they are happy to be oyster farmers.

Eric and Valy's year follows a cycle of planting seeds. Tending them. Transferring tiny seedlings to a nursery and then the larger seedlings to a grow-out plot. In late May, they obtained oyster seed about the size of a baby's fingernail from Marshall Point Sea Farm, in Port Clyde, and from Muscongus Bay Aquaculture,

Opposite & Below: All photos courtesy of Flying Point Oysters (Fred Field)

in Bremen. These are placed in upwellers installed in dock-like structures built for the purpose. The docks are put in an 8-square-foot space rented at a marina. They serve a second function by providing additional tie-up space for small boats. Water is circulated through the upwellers by a small motor. This provides a rich source of nutrients for the seeds, which quickly increase in size.

During the summer, Eric and Valy flip the oyster bags to let the sun dry, and thus kill, the algae that collects on the side that has been in the water. This improves water flow through the bag. They also remove small oyster drills from the bags, as well as starfish. Oyster drills are snails that prey on oysters, attacking them by making small holes through the oysters' shells. And if the couple fail to remove a starfish, says Eric, "By the end of the season, you have this big fat happy starfish and no oysters."

"An entrepreneur is a person who works 24 hours a day for himself to avoid having to work 8 hours a day for someone else."

—*Eric Horne*

Right: Maquoit Bay (Bill Perna)

Adam Campbell
North Haven Oysters

"I grew up in a small town on the Hudson River, Croton-On-Hudson, in New York. When I came here to Maine in 1986, I was 20. I talked to a lot of the older fishermen. I asked them what they thought the lobster fishing season was going to be like? The reply was 'Adam, I've been fishing for 57 years and I've never seen the same season twice'. That tells you how variable a fishing season can be.

"You're working with the rhythm of the ocean and that's a unique way to live. When I was younger it was the hunter-gatherer way

Opposite: Abel LaBelle bags oysters on the Salt Pond in North Haven (Seth Macy)

Above: Adam Campbell of North Haven Oyster (Seth Macy)

of life and getting paid every day instead of waiting for a check at the end of the week; being your own boss, having your own boat, being your own captain, no one telling you what to do.

"But the Gulf of Maine is changing, the water temperature is rising, and lobsters are really super-sensitive to temperature. When the water gets above a certain temperature, the lobsters just move off. I had five young kids in the house. I had a boat payment, big house payment, and if I had one little blip, you know, if I had a bad year, I could have lost the house. This land has been in my wife's family since the 1760s, so I didn't want to screw that up.

"The town hired a marine biologist to come to North Haven Island here in the Penobscot Bay to figure out why our smelts disappeared. We used to have smelts out here. He came to this estuary and said: 'This isn't a good spot for raising smelts, but someone ought to try growing an oyster here.' So, I decided I would diversify and start an oyster farm just to hedge my bets in case there was a downturn in lobstering. I started in 1999, when we didn't even have the Internet out here. I killed a lot of oysters. I fed a lot of green crabs… (But) It was great having my family work with me. I just can't think of any other way I'd want to make a living."

"Some people are just made to work outdoors. You know, I've been cold, I've been beat up, I've been hurt, but that makes you feel alive."

—Adam Campbell

"Maine lobstermen and commercial fishing families have turned to aquaculture to boost revenue and diversify their businesses. According to data from the Department of Marine Resources, roughly 50 commercial lobster license holders also hold aquaculture leases, meaning that one in every six Maine aquaculturists also captains a lobster boat."

—Sebastian Belle
Executive Director of the
Maine Aquaculture
Association

Dan Devereaux
Mere Point Oyster Co.

I drove out towards the end of Mere Point, on Maquoit Bay. It was one of those crisp sunny days in February that makes you happy to be in the Pine Tree State. I arrived at the Mere Point oyster barn a little early. Looking around the yard, I saw neatly stacked oyster-growing cages, oyster bags, lobster traps and a beautiful lobster boat named "Miss Nicole II," put up for the winter.

I couldn't help but laugh at the irony that a group of people who were very vocal in trying to stop Mere Point Oysters from getting an oyster lease argued that they wanted to protect lobstermen's interests. The two sons of Doug Niven, a Mere Point Oysters partner, are commercial lobstermen. Dan Devereaux greeted me. He is a big, strong guy who looked very capable of making

short work of splitting the pile of wood behind him. Like many Mainers he is direct and says what he means.

The Maine Department of Marine Resources recently issued a draft approval of Mere Point Oyster Farm after the firm had to battle some neighbors who objected to the firm's plan for a 40-acre farm on Maquoit Bay. The group used various strategies and tactics. For example, they put up signs of "Stop the Oyster Factory" and "No Plastic Sunsets." They hired a PR person who developed an ill-conceived strategy that states, disingenuously, that the neighbors don't object to oyster aquaculture *per se* but rather are only interested in "preserving Maine's fishing heritage." But most lobstermen are completely unaware of the group, which named itself Protect Maine's Fishing Heritage, perhaps because many of its members are "From Away" and those lobstermen who *are* aware of it wonder how much its members know about the issues that fishermen face, particularly global warming, that imperil traditional wild-caught fishing, including lobstering.

Dan told me: "I've been a local Marine Resources warden for 23 years. I retired in 2018. Now I'm a coastal-resource manager for the same town (Brunswick). I have two jobs. I couldn't do oyster farming and have just one job. When Doug Niven, my partner, and I really started to put our heads together about starting an oyster farm we both approached our families to talk about the idea and their interest in supporting it. We were thinking about the changes in the ocean and the decline in wild fisheries in our bays. Fishing activity has declined in the past decade and a half.

Above Left: Dan Devereaux (Mere Point Oyster Co.)

Opposite: Photo by Bill Perna

Photo by Bill Perna

"The fishermen who fished pogies (a fish used for bait in lobster traps) don't come into Maquoit Bay as much as they used to; the fish are no longer plentiful. Lobstermen used to fish the channels up into the bay until the water became so warm. You don't see those guys as much. Coastal properties are being sold, and small camps are being replaced with large summer vacation homes by people from away seeking their own slice of coastal Maine scenery. We are seeing the decline in our ocean resources. We see the water-warming trends that are not stopping. And then you think about shellfish and their ecological benefit and value they provide to the environment. Our bay used to have a lot of shellfish, i.e., mussels, soft-shell clams, European and American oysters, and the filtration (by the shellfish) used to be there, but with the declines the bay is being filtered less and less each year. Doug and I started to think that shellfish aquaculture is something that we need to invest in for coastal resilience in the face of climate change. We need to find ways to put people to

work, to put young local people back to work on the water.

"I worry about what happens if we don't find replacement work on the water. You know, ships and steamboats used to come up here with goods and supplies. We have a historic shipbuilding site at the base of Mere Point Peninsula. The surrounding working waters are the fabric and history of our community. And when you start to tear away that fabric, you rip apart the history and the foundation our community is built on. And we talked a lot about the environmental impacts. That's one of the major reasons why we started Mere Point Oyster.

"When I look back six years and think about when we first started growing oysters and started being advocates for sustainable shellfish farming…. I'm not sure I would do it again. I'm not sure I'd put my family through that process again. One of the critical things was the pushback that we had from people that wanted to stop our lease. Our lease is in one of the most ecologically responsible areas in Maquoit Bay.

"After 23 years as a local marine warden, I know where the ecologically sensitive areas are. I know where the channels are. And it was funny because one of the issues in our lease hearing that the lobsterman brought up was that they fished the area that we wanted to farm. No, they don't: It's seven feet deep at low tide with a mud bottom.

"When we initially proposed farming this area, some people opposed our proposal and put up signs that said, 'Stop the Oyster Factory.' 'No Plastic Sunsets'. There were many public platforms and social-media outlets they tried to manipulate with misinformation. Some people were adamantly against our oyster-farm proposal, mostly those shoreline owners that look onto oyster farms.

"Understanding climate change is actually pretty easy," Devereaux said. "It's chemistry and physics. If you understand chemistry and physics, then you understand what is happening and what needs to happen to help mitigate the change.

"Many people don't understand the difficulty of oyster farming in an open-bay environment, especially when the weather is rough. You need enough space between your gear to avoid gear failures and tangle ups. You have to have gear protections that you don't need in a river system like the Damariscotta where it's protected because it's narrow. It is two miles-plus across Maquoit Bay. … Then there are the regulatory challenges.

"Both of my partner Doug Niven's sons are lobstermen. Their lobster catch was way down this past summer (of 2018). They both are able to come to work at Mere Point Oysters and remain working on the water where they have grown up and love so much."

Dan continued: "Oyster aquaculture needs a much stronger presence. Shellfish aquaculture is going to mitigate some of the impacts of climate change. It's as simple as that. I hope that people begin to connect these facts with the need for shellfish aquaculture. I guess when the impact is in your backyard, it becomes nimbyism. The same folks that oppose our oyster farm are the same folks that cut down trees and fertilize their lawns, and often they just happen to also be the big donors to some of the largest nonprofit environmental groups in the state and country. So I guess it's okay if you have enough money you can mitigate your own pollution through monetary contributions.

These are the same people who have run my credibility through the mud. Think of the irony of that.

"I don't know how many people we've helped start shellfish-aquaculture operations in this town and in other parts of the state. A lot of people come to us. Sharing information is a great thing about the industry. I can call Bill Mook and say: 'I know you have a lot of experience on this or that. Can you tell me the best way that we could probably do this for our area?' And then we are able to share that information at our local level.

"We go every year and give a presentation about oyster aquaculture to every junior high student in Brunswick. We have worked with many different people that have started oyster farms

Courtesy of New England Ocean Cluster

all around. This is important. We need to encourage people to take up oyster farming. We need to help spread support for this type of sustainable and climate-mitigating ocean farming.

"Our families are going to be raised right here in Brunswick. And after college they're going to come back and guess what? They're going to contribute to the community that they grew up in." Doug's family owned the Times Record, the local daily paper, Devereaux noted to me. (Doug retired from the paper when his family sold it.)

"I believe aquaculture is something we need for our local community. We have 61 miles of coastline, 20 miles of river frontage along the Androscoggin River. That means we're very susceptible to climate change. We have sea-level rise coming…

"Right now, the shellfish industry in Brunswick has 66 people working as clam diggers…These guys are working hard and there's lots that is at stake for them on these mud flats. To keep that kind of tradition of near-shore fishery alive we need shellfish aquaculture. It's as simple as that.

"We had a pretty big informational meeting at the Brunswick Public Library for interested people about the Maquoit Bay environment and our oyster-farming proposal. We also provided this information at our lease hearing. We have invested significant effort and resources to educate local people. We brought in marine biologists and scientists to talk about the ecosystem in Maquoit Bay. Nutrient intrusion into the bay is a huge concern. And if we don't have a filtration system in this bay to filter those nutrients, we're going to get algal blooms which kill off a lot of things by depleting the oxygen in the water. It has already happened on different parts of our shore. The mussels that used to be out here, just 15 years ago, have been pushed out by climate change. And dragging for mussels impacted the fragile eelgrass meadows in the upper bay; each species near shore is linked to others.If you break the links the ecosystem gets out of balance, and this really impacts the natural process that allows the bay to flourish. You can only imagine what the impacts are of the billions of shellfish lost to fishing or changes in the habitat due to climate change. That's like taking a swimming pool filter out of your pool in July.

"Development and impervious surfaces cause increased runoff, and with that come all the nutrients that trigger a lot of additional impacts. We need to have shellfish to filter and consume them. For instance, the house right down the street has a few cottages that come along with it. All those places have septic systems, and septic systems have a tendency to seep over the years, especially when they are used more and more each year. They are old systems. Everything on Mere Point, in Brunswick, is built on a big rock ledge. Unless we want to slow down development, and I'm sure that's not what the town wants to do because they're hurting for tax dollars, we are caught in this Catch-22.

"I live in a silo. Sometimes it's hard for me to understand why people can't see the writing on the wall. Then I realize they must also live in their own silo. It's important to be able to come outside of that silo, and number one, trust science, trust academia, trust what Governor Mills is trying to do right now with the Climate Council initiative. Trust that shellfish farming is an adaptive practice being used by working watermen, fishermen and academia to help mitigate climate impacts that have been scientifically proven to be part of our future."

Opposite: Photo by Bill Perna

THE NEW BLUE TECH ENTREPRENEURS

This is generally a younger crowd (though not all of them),
driven at times by environmental ideals and a bit of romance.
They want to earn their living on the water and know that oysters
are sustainable and help clean coastal waters.

These people include the likes of John Herrigel, who started
the Maine Oyster Co.; Ben Hamilton, of Love Point Oysters;
Jordan Kramer, of Winnegance Oysters; Abby Barrows, of Long
Cove Sea Farm, in Deer Isle, and Ryan McPherson, who bought
Glidden Point Oysters Farms in 2016, among many others.

They embrace new strategies and technological innovation, with
a vision of the ocean as a source of new opportunity that will
attract investors to help bring these solutions to scale.

Opposite: Courtesy of Community Shellfish

Community Shellfish
Owned by Boe Marsh
Bremen, Maine

I had heard about Boe Marsh's ideas at Community Shellfish Co., in Bremen, aimed at helping to re-energize Maine's working waterfront. That led to a visit and a chance to enjoy some of the Cora Cressy oysters he was growing.

I arrived at Community Shellfish, at Keene Narrows on Muscongus Bay's western shore, beautiful even by Maine standards. The water is crowded with lobster boats. I was reminded of a quote from Joshua Slocum's *Sailing Around the World Alone* about when he sailed into nearby Round Pond

Above: Boe Marsh (Tristan Spinski, New York Times)

Opposite: Courtesy of Community Shellfish

Harbor in 1895: "The wind being free, I ran into Round Pond Harbour, which is a little port east of Pemaquid. Here I rested for a day while the wind rattled among the pine trees on the shore."

One immediately notices a large wooden hull sticking out of the water -- the hull of the Cora Cressy, a famous five-masted, 273-feet-long freight schooner that was operated in the coasting trade. It was built in 1902, by the Percy and Small Yard in Bath, Maine, and was in service until 1928. For a time after that it was a floating nightclub. Then she was towed to the Keene Narrows and scuttled to serve as a breakwater for the lobster operation. It remains one of the largest surviving wooden hulls in the United States and is listed on the National Register of Historic Places.

It was there that I met Boe Marsh. He was fixing a pump on an upweller, a device that brings up nutrients in the water to feed large quantities of oyster seed.

"I'm a native Vermonter," he told me. "When I was five years old my family moved to Hartford, Connecticut. Then we moved to Greenwich, Connecticut. I went to the University of Vermont back in Burlington. My major was anthropology. I was a big skier and I worked Out West for a while. Then I came back East and got a career in international finance on Wall Street.

"My specialty was South Africa. I dealt with the political risk of Apartheid. After a while I left Merrill Lynch and Deutsche Bank

"The hell with this. I don't want to die in a gray-flannel suit in Greenwich, Connecticut."

—Boe Marsh

and founded my own firm. We hoped that we were instrumental in financing new businesses in the new South Africa, the majority/minority businesses. Then I sold that company to the South African bank Absa Group Ltd., in 2000. Then I worked for a hedge fund for a couple of years until I said to myself: "The hell with this. I don't want to die in a gray-flannel suit in Greenwich, Conn."

"I moved to Maine in 2004 and became a builder. I built my own house. And I built a building that had a processing room with a lobster tank down on the shore for a group of lobstermen and their lobster co-op, the Bremen Co-op. The Bremen Co-op was founded in 1995. We became friends and they asked me to join their co-op as an employee to promote their business and to develop the processing arm, which I did. We collaborated for the next couple of years. Then they decided in 2011 they didn't want to do processing anymore because of the economic downturn. Lobster prices got clobbered, down to $1.45 a pound. and oil went through the roof. They offered me the business. I accepted and told them, 'I will rent from you and take the volatility out of your business. I will take the business risk.' They loved that idea. We have collaborated ever since. Later, they decided to sell me both the land and the lobster facility. They trusted me with this beautiful asset that we have here. And so, in 2016, I bought this property."

What if you hadn't gotten involved in Bremen Co-op?

"Well, that's hard to say. These are very capable people. They know what they are doing. One reason they wanted me to keep the Bremen Co-op going is they saw how I operated. If I hadn't

Opposite: Fog rolls in at Keenan Narrows in Bremen (Bill Perna)

CORA F. CRESSEY, painted by Solon Badger; on display in the Maine Maritime Museum, Bath, Maine.

been there they might still own it. If they sold it, it would have been another buyer who, like me, understood that this is a working waterfront and is such a valuable asset. This is not only a financial asset as a piece of property but it is important to the families and the community and the fishing industry at large. If the wrong buyer had come in and developed the property, taking this working waterfront out of its current use, it would have been disastrous for the local seafood industry and the broader community in the Bremen area."

Vision for Creating an Aquaculture Hub

"Aquaculture, like any other industry, needs to scale to be commercially viable. You need reasonably large production to make it viable. We know that using an aluminum skiff, a town landing and a pickup truck isn't going to make much of a dent in the larger supply chain with oysters, kelp or whatever you're growing.

"So what does an independent grower need to scale? You need infrastructure, and where do you get infrastructure? You get infrastructure on the working waterfront. The problem is that not everybody has access to a working waterfront. The viability of aquaculture depends on the independent grower, large and small. The diversity and number of independent farms leads to lower volatility in the supply chain. Just like a Midwestern farming community that shares a grain silo and sells to the highest bidder. It is the same here. We are going to provide that silo to aquaculturists.

"We have more than 3,400 miles of coastline in Maine, but infrastructure is not available to everyone. There is a new generation of maritime activities, including aquaculture, that will need available shoreline infrastructure. Our vision is beginning to be successful. We want to make our Bremen working waterfront a hub for aquaculture, attracting growers who want to pursue aquaculture on a larger commercial scale. We have coolers and freezers and shore-side storage as well as a stone dock where trucks can pick up and drop off material. We have two Hyster booms to lift and lower. We have parking and land for equipment storage. Our goal is to provide this, not only for ourselves but for other growers as well. We see this as a potential up and down the Maine coast. Lobster fishing has become more volatile and unpredictable. We want to see other lobster dealerships and docks provide services for aquaculture.

"We provide infrastructure on the production side and diversity of choice for our customers. As an example, on our Website we have six oyster farms partnering with us. We market and sell all those oysters. And we include descriptions of the oyster varieties and contacts."

"We partner with Heron Island Oyster Co.'s Colin Brannon. He's a great grower who has focused on small-scale surface culture. We also have Swan's Island Oyster Farm, with Jason Joyce and Josh Joyce, and Iron Island Oyster, in New Meadows, with Dana Morris and John Swenson. We have a partner, Ray Koniski, who's a small grower. We upwell his oyster seedlings for him. We also partner with Gary Gentner, who's a burgeoning farmer just getting going. He's also a lobsterman here. The Medomak Oysters are our oysters. We also have the Cora Cressy Oysters.

"A vertically integrated system is our goal. That system enables businesses like ours to get the maximum return when we take something out of the water and put it in somebody's mouth.

"We wholesale a lot of stuff. Some of our big wholesale customers are the big names like Sysco, US Foods, Gordon Foods, Dennis Foods and North Coast Seafoods. Our biggest cash flow really does consist of our wholesale."

How does it all work?

"There's no financial agreement between Community Shellfish and the lobstermen. They are individual contractors who choose to fish here and sell their stuff to us. As individual contractors they can pick up all their stuff and take off tomorrow. They sell us their lobsters. Period. In return, we provide them with parking, moorings, fuel sales, bait sales, a place to store their traps in the winter. And the most important thing is that we guarantee them -- six days a week, Monday through Saturday -- a ready market for their lobsters.

Opposite: Fog lifting in Keenan Narrows in Bremen (Bill Perna)

"We have four lines of businesses -- selling lobsters, clams and aquaculture oysters and sharing this infrastructure for a fee. We're looking for partners who will come in and use our infrastructure. This might include, say, lobstermen who are becoming oyster farmers.

"We're looking to build this hub. We have a lot of partners using this spot like it is a village. We're all trading off sales, technology and gear. Very symbiotic. And as a result, everybody does better. We are trying to build everyone's strengths through strategic alliances.

"This is my vision for this place. And it comes back to how important access to working waterfront is.

"We really need to dynamize the coast of Maine. The wild-caught fisheries need to be respected and aquaculture needs to be fostered. It's all about making Maine a more viable place. Maine's produce and what comes out of our waters are absolutely the best stuff in the world for health. And we all know that you can't farm for corn and feed it to cows and get the amount of protein that's needed. Aquaculture can help meet this need."

Distribution System

"Community Shellfish is very integrated. We deal in a variety of species -- oysters, clams, mussels and scallops, and we're beginning to grow quahogs.

"We all went through Maine and into Massachusetts. And we are branching out to put brick and mortar down at a facility we

Opposite: Aerial of Keenan Narrows (Courtesy of Community Shellfish)

plan in Fairfield County, Connecticut, as a distribution center, retail store and wine and oyster bar. This will be very valuable, to our company and our partners and to other growers who would become part of our shared space.

"Besides Community Shellfish seafood, we're going to bring other Maine products down there. Maine is very hot in Connecticut, as we all know, sort of like Vermont was 15 years ago. All of our customers have said, 'Look, if it's got Maine on it, they want it.'

"We're also looking to create an 'in-between client' between wholesale and retail. I mean the high-end customer willing to pay more for the sea-to-table product.

"You know, oyster aquaculture, clamming, lobstering, etc., are not easy. People should be rewarded for their work. Maine has an important asset. We want to monetize this asset more than it has been and that includes a fair price for our stuff.

"The wholesalers have been in the habit for years of just screwing the producer by paying as little as possible and turning around and getting most of the value added for themselves, usually out of state."

Future of Maine's Working Waterfront

"The important thing about the working waterfront is this: This is a *shared* workplace. Our facility is like a big office complex for maritime people. Fishermen and their families keep a lot of their belongings here. It is a nexus for all kinds of activities -- fishing, working in other ways, and community. It's important to preserve it, but in this case, preservation is accomplished by revitalizing and empowering it.

"Harvesting wild-caught species is becoming more volatile and unreliable. Aquaculture can help offset the decline of wild-caught fishing. These are additions, not replacements, for finfish fishing, lobsters, etc. Aquaculture is going to give people many income streams. Which is the traditional way on the Maine Coast.

"I remember 10 years ago when there were important species to be caught along the Maine coast whose numbers have since declined, such as shrimp, finfish and urchins. The main surviving wild-caught species is lobster. There is also still clamming. But the working waterfront needs more opportunities for people to make a living there. That's where aquaculture comes in."

Challenges Facing Aquaculturists & Fishermen in Maine

"The challenges are (1) rights to use the ocean for *both* riparian and wild-caught fisheries; (2) access to working-waterfront infrastructure and (3) water quality.

"Luckily for us, we are the last guardian of good water. There are problems in Cape Cod and the Chesapeake Bay. Florida is a wreck and the West Coast is having problems. Still, we have a high risk of water-quality problems with bacteria and with red tide. But the Maine Department of Marine Resources (DMR) is handling that very well. Meanwhile, people should remember aquaculture is still a young industry and it's a big world.

"We have a well-run state Department of Marine Resources under Commissioner Patrick Keliher. With regulations, enforcement, getting oyster farmers on the water, they are very good. They understand what we're doing in aquaculture, and what our challenges are. The DMR is behind us. And when they make a judgment on an aquaculture lease, whether it's an experimental or standard, they are very fair.

"Our lease hearing was on September 15 (2020) to get our oyster aquaculture 20-year standard lease." Boe said the hearing went well.

"The main impediments to aquaculture are access to infrastructure, climate change and markets that have not evolved enough for taking large volumes of aquaculture products out of Maine."

Biggest Challenges in Marketing Maine Aquaculture

"We have two tiers of buyers for aquaculture products. One is people willing to pay a fair price for great products and understand what they're getting. Another tier, as I've noted, is out-of-state companies coming in and buying our raw materials, at very low costs, and then taking them out of state and getting most of the value-added. We need better organized marketing and sales teams.

"We have to look at other successful marketing and sales collaborations to see what works. A good example is the Bordeaux wine region, in France. There are currently 60 appellations in the region.

"There are 5,000-bottle and a million-bottle chateaux but only a handful of truly different grapes and a handful of different wines. But they sell tons of wine every year. How do they do that? They differentiate among micro-regions and terroirs. They all support each other by supporting and promoting the appellations, and by distinguishing among the flavors and the grape varieties. Each terroir is celebrated for its individual quality. This is a viable strategy for Maine oysters. Each of our coastal rivers imparts different tastes. For aquaculture we just switch 'terroir' with 'merroir.'"

Julie Qiu has said that "The Damariscotta is the Napa Valley of oysters."

"Yes, it kind of is. The Damariscotta is the biggest production area, with the most organized selling organization and its quality is A1. We are the Côte d'Or here. Smaller production and a very high-quality product. Swan's Island provides the Willamette Valley of oysters. Again, this is not a 'better than' discussion. It is about celebrating the differences among Maine oysters."

The Future of Maine Aquaculture

"Either it will remain a small eclectic group of growers or it's going to be something big. Again, I emphasize the importance of having working-waterfront infrastructure for serving aquaculturists. It's the only way we're going to get anywhere; people need access. The other side of it is how well we do at marketing as part of promoting a broad appreciation of the value of Maine seafood.

"Maine needs to aggressively develop a marketing plan but not with a big government role as in France. We need a state trade association organized so that people don't have to say that this oyster is better than that one but that every oyster from Maine has a unique flavor.

"All this reminds me that when Maine cedar is exported to Quebec it's sold for peanuts. It's then made into shingles, and it comes back out after it's been painted and dipped and sold back to people in the United States for huge value-added. So, we here in Maine have lost most of the value added."

Climate Change

"Aquaculture is the perfect hedge against warming water and other water-quality issues. Water quality is a direct descendant of climate change. As the wild-caught fisheries become more volatile, it becomes more difficult to predict catch.

"Look at the shrimp landings. There are no more shrimp in Maine. The waters are too warm here. All the shrimp are off Canada now. And in 10 years, it will be too warm up there. That's just one fishery. Soft-shell clams is another industry that's really being affected. They're being ravaged by predators that like warm water: green crabs, snails, worms. Everybody loves warm water, including the predators. Green crabs eat the baby clams. It's practically impossible to protect against them. So we went into aquaculture, a business that made sense to me in buying this property.'

Glidden Point Oyster Farms
Owned by Ryan McPherson
Damariscotta River, Maine

"Barbara Scully founded Glidden Point Oyster Farms in 1987. Barbara was a marine biologist. She operated Glidden Point Oyster Farms for about 30 years, and I took over in the 2016 season," McPherson told me.

"I was looking for an opportunity to grow oysters. I met Barbara Scully and we began a discussion of how I could create that

opportunity. It took a couple of years to figure out how to make the transition. But we did it. And 2016 was my first growing season here.

"I was always trying to find a home working on the water. And I was involved with almost all the fisheries I could work with. The fisheries are changing so fast. New aquaculture was my home. I was looking for an opportunity to grow really good oysters.

"I come from Massachusetts. There are a lot of oyster farms there and a lot of great oysters. But I was looking for something a step above that. I knew that the estuaries like the Damariscotta River could create the best oysters in the world.

"We get our seed from hatcheries. We work with two great hatcheries here in Maine, the best in the country. They are neighbors; they also farm right next to us. When you get those seeds, they are about two millimeters big. We get those in June. We're sorting by size every day until September. When September comes, they should be about two inches big. We'll take those oysters down river four miles and plant those in the coldest,

deepest water we can find for our crop. We'll put them on the bottom for two years. Then by the third year, we'll harvest the oysters.

"We put the oysters in the deep cold water because that's really the makeup of the shell and the tastes that you will taste at the table wherever you are. The colder the water, the better the oyster will be. It will be denser, heartier meat.

"I couldn't live without being on the water. To see the full life cycle of oysters is the most rewarding thing I've come across. Our employees are so intrigued by the process - the whole ethos around it and growing something. Delivering it to the end consumer and the value that it creates. Their interests bring them here every morning to see how to grow that product and deliver it.

"There are more people calling for oysters, so we will produce more oysters for the wider market. But there's also growth within our own retail shop. More and more consumers are coming here to the farm."

"You have to listen to what your crops are telling you and most of the time, to slow it down. The hardest part of growing is waiting for the oysters to be perfect."

—Ryan McPherson

Below & Opposite: Courtesy of Glidden Point Oyster Farms

Maine Ocean Farms
Co-owned by Eric Oransky
Casco Bay, Maine

Eric Oransky grew up in Freeport, Maine. He spent a lot of time on Casco Bay. And he grew up taking stuff apart to see how things worked. He has worked in carpentry since he was 14. When he was 21 he apprenticed with the Scottish master cabinet maker James Bowie for furniture making in northern California. In 2007, at 23, Eric moved back to Maine and started his first business, all the while spending time on the water any chance he got. He focused on wood working, including furniture, and building for about seven years. He found he missed working on the water. So in 2017 he formed Maine Ocean Farms with his two partners, Willy Leathers and Tom Klodenski. All are still in their 30's.

He told me: "I met Willy Leathers and Tom Klodenski while working on sail-training and research programs for Ocean Classroom and the At Sea Education Association. We sailed tall ships from Maine to South America, Northeast Atlantic, Mediterranean and around New Zealand. We would take middle-school to college-age students out to sea for trips from one week to four months. We would teach them how to sail, navigate, including celestial navigation, work as a team, and learn some science."

How did you come to think oyster aquaculture was a good idea?

"In early 2017 Willy and I learned about the Maine Superior Court ruling on wild harvesting of seaweed. The court ruled that public's rights to privately owned tidelands are limited only to those enumerated in a 1647 colonial ordinance -- that is, fishing, fowling, and navigation -- and that harvesting seaweed did not count as fishing. That ruling effectively ended the industry that harvested wild seaweed. We realized there would be a seaweed-supply shortage and saw that as an opportunity to grow our own seaweed. That would let us continue to earn a living on the water without having to ship out for four months to New Zealand, the other side of the world, every year. I love New Zealand but I had gotten tired of traveling so far over the previous four winters."

"Willy and I were pretty certain that we wanted to start a

Opposite: Sunrise, end of September. Headed out for a day in the wheel house. Willy Leathers at the helm. (Eric Oransky)

Above Left: Eric Oransky giving a tour of the farm to the Eventide restaurant staff. "Maine Ocean Farms offers tours to all of our restaurant partners so that we can share our story. The restaurant tours are a lot of fun and usually involve eating lots of oysters." (Courtesy of Eventide)

seaweed-aquaculture operation. We applied to the Island Institute's Aquaculture Business Development (ABD) program, in Rockland, Maine, and were both accepted. The day after I got home from New Zealand, we drove up to Rockland and had the first of many meetings. The ABD program is comprehensive. We learned how to grow kelp, oysters and mussels. We read studies by Maine state government experts and the Maine Aquaculture Association and looked at growth projections, capital requirements and economies of scale for growing kelp, oysters and mussels. We studied rates of return on investments, the market for these products, and indeed, the entire working process for the sector. We began to realize that oysters, not kelp, was the way for us to build a viable business.

"Oyster aquaculture had moderate capital requirements and the market was solid. But we worried about how to differentiate ourselves. The return for oysters is based on a per-piece price, as opposed to a pounds or volume. Growing oysters would keep us busy for most of the year. And there was the added advantage that we could put the oysters on the bottom for the winter and still go out to sea if we wanted. So for the first three years of this operation, we would sink the oysters in December and then I would fly to New Zealand, get on a ship, and work for the next three and a half months. Then I'd come home and within a week or two it was time to bring the oysters back up."

What are some of the biggest challenges for Maine oyster agriculture?

"We need to do a better job of educating communities about aquaculture. A lot of people don't quite understand what oyster aquaculture is, especially those who live along the water. There needs to be good communication and collaboration with other

The Maine Ocean Farms original founders: Tom Klondenski, Eric Oransky and Willy Leathers (Aaron Turkel)

commercial-fishing operations, in particular lobstering. We need to ensure that we can work in proximity, without interfering with each other, and explain the potential benefits of having oysters in the inner bays and coves of Maine, especially that oysters clean the water.

"And we don't need to interfere with a viable commercial fishing ground for lobster. We've been very proactive, and the lobstermen were the first people to see what our plans were at every stage so that we could know their concerns when developing our plan.

"The lobster hauls have been down and the price hasn't been

great. I have a good friend who is a lobsterman. Every time I see him, he says. 'I'm thinking about getting into oysters, seaweed and scallops.' I don't think he is quite ready, but soon."

Talk about Maine Ocean Farms' Wet Smack Oyster Shell

"Between the time we decided to go into oyster aquaculture and when we put our first oyster seed into the water and through the first year, we asked for a lot of input from chefs and from other folks who are oyster connoisseurs. What type of oyster do you look for? If you could design an oyster, what would be its best characteristics? And then, we set out to create that oyster., We studied oysters grown around the world. We looked at those aesthetics and flavor characteristics and tried to figure out what will stand out -- unique oysters that aren't going to get lost in the flood of new oyster operations. Something that is clean, consistent, easy to shuck and tastes good.

"Those were the criteria that led us to the idea we needed a different process or a variation of an existing process to produce something that looks very different. We wanted an oyster that if you set a bunch of oysters out next to each other, ours will stand out. Wet Smack Oysters are very clearly different from the rest. Wet Smacks are very uniform in size and shape with smooth edges, thick, clean shells and a very deep cup. They are handled a lot to keep them so smooth, round and uniform so the shell is much smaller than most oysters of the same age in Casco Bay but there is just as much oyster inside. Sometimes it's almost overflowing when you shuck them.

"Our oysters go through a lot of extra handling and tumbling and grading. We handle them more frequently than most farmers do. It's labor-intensive. And so more expensive than most oysters. We use all surface gear in the summer and not the big 'OysterGro' cages, but the soft floating bags, and with exposure to wind and wave action on our site. There's more agitation. We have exposure to the southwest, from which comes the prevailing summer winds, all the way up Broad Sound. So we get that one-to-two-foot chop that churns the oysters all the time. Being in the soft floating bags means that we're almost always in the top two to three inches of the water where the sunlight penetrates. This keeps the shells very clean.

"And then in the late fall/early winter, we put the bags of oysters into overwintering cages that are dropped to the bottom. We selected the best possible sites to grow them. We were looking for really clean water with temperatures that get high enough in the summer to allow enough oyster growth so that the economics worked out better. The longer it takes to grow them, the more you have to handle them, and so the more expensive it is to produce a single oyster. We got maps for the northwest end of Casco Bay of water-sampling data from the state for the last 20 years. We were able to determine from spreadsheets and maps what we could expect the water temperatures would be and for how long. Then we could determine what months would need the most labor, and when the oysters would grow the fastest.

"We are in an area with very clean water and insulated from rain closures --- in Recompense Cove in Freeport, between Wolf Neck and Flying Point. Wolf Neck State Forest and Wolf Neck Farm are the two largest waterfront pieces in our growing area. Our science team from the Island Institute's Aquaculture Business Development Program recommended that site selection after water-quality sampling. We are also only a mile from the Freeport Harbor, where we already had water access when we started, including mooring and slips. We know some of the lobstermen there and having grown up in Freeport, we also knew enough people who live on the shoreline to be able to initiate those conversations. We make sure that we can inform those people about what we're doing and give them the opportunity to ask questions, express concerns and make sure they know that we are committed to finding ways to allow everyone to enjoy, and, for some, work on the water.

"People called us a lot in the first year wanting to know what was going on. We would give them a 30-minute education on aquaculture. We've also held private meetings for folks who couldn't attend our information sessions. We chose a site right in the middle of the bay, Recompense Cove, so that we are about 2,000 feet from the nearest shoreline; if you're less than a thousand feet the law requires you to notify riparian landowners. We just put ourselves as far away from everybody as we could so that nobody has to look at it any more than necessary, and we use low-profile gear. In addition, we talked with the lobstermen about the orientation of our long lines to avoid entanglements.

"When we were developing our design for our standard lease at that location before anyone else saw a draft, the guys who actually fished commercially there sat down with us, with the drawings, and gave their input. And we shifted our design to accommodate their concerns."

What's been the progress since you started in April of 2017?

"In the fall of 2018, our first oysters came to market size. We did a trial with a few restaurants where we knew the chefs and we had solicited comments. We gave away a lot of oysters and would shuck oysters for people. If there was a small private party, we would give oysters to people and ask them to fill out an online review form we had created.

"We got a lot of feedback. They were saying, 'These oysters are so amazing. Wet Smacks are the best oysters I've ever had.' We took that feedback with a grain of salt. After all, it was from friends and other people we knew and we had given them the oysters. But in the spring/early summer, 2019 we had oysters ready to market. So we went to Big Tree Hospitality, which owns Eventide Oyster Co., in Portland, among other very good restaurants.

"I met with Andrew Taylor, a Big Tree owner. I brought four dozen oysters down to their operation in Biddeford. Andrew and his team tried them. Everybody seemed to really like them. Andrew then brought our oysters to Eventide and shared them there. The next day they called to say they wanted to buy 400 oysters per week. And a few days later I got another call from Andrew. He told us he wanted to bring our oysters along with Glidden Point and Winter Points to serve at the dinner at the James Beard Awards in Chicago. The James Beard Awards honors chefs and other leaders who make America's food culture more delicious, diverse and sustainable for everyone.

"Andrew said: 'We'd like to showcase your oysters. Wet Smack oysters may be among the most unique oysters we have available to us. And we'd like to take them with us.' And that was the point where we were kind of stunned. Maybe all the feedback wasn't people just being nice. Maybe we grew an oyster that is really special. We now sell Eventide a thousand oysters a week. And they go through the oysters in about three days.

"We started distributing through Sopo Seafood, in Biddeford.

They sell our larger Recompense Cove Oysters to restaurants, and the Wet Smacks for local-delivery customer pickup, and ship them anywhere in the country overnight.

"We picked about a half dozen key restaurants in Maine we wanted to be in. We didn't go around to every restaurant and say, 'Here's a dozen of our oysters. Try them.' After tasting them, all the restaurants bought our oysters."

How did Wet Smacks get their name?

"The first Wet Smacks were sailing vessels with holes drilled below the waterline of the fish hold, allowing sea water to flow through keeping fresh seafood alive and in prime condition for market. In the 1830s, Mainers began to use Wet Smacks to transport live lobster to Boston and New York, marking the beginning of Maine's commercial lobster industry."

Other things I should ask?

"Willy (Leathers) and I are Coast Guard-licensed captains. We sailed together on the same ships. That gave us a different background coming into aquaculture. Knowing how to work on the water and having solid communication, recordkeeping, organizational skills and management experience has been a key factor in our success. The operational conditions of working in Casco Bay, even the worst possible day, is nothing like what we've seen working offshore. The inner bay rarely has higher than three-to-four-foot waves.

"Willy is also a shipwright and handy in many other areas. My background has been working as a contractor, doing woodworking, including furniture making, running my

These Wet Smacks were headed to Eventide, Gather, Royal River Grill House and SoPo Seafood. (Eric Oransky)

"Farming oysters is a strange business. You have to know how to build stuff, fix stuff, engineer stuff, design stuff, and how to work efficiently on the water."

—*Eric Oransky*

own business, and doing CAD drawings, logistical planning, supervising employees, and dealing with contractors and subcontractors. Keeping people happy and on schedule and knowing how to use the equipment.

"We can buy an old beat-up boat and rewire the whole thing ourselves and fix the engine. We divided the operational and managerial sides of the business into parts. We set it up so we could focus and maintain continuity across the platforms.

"It's somewhat like farming on land, except that, unlike with most land crops, it takes two to three years for the crop to get ripe. And, as with all farming, you have to expect the unexpected. There's that Donald Rumsfeld line about 'the known unknowns and the unknown unknowns.' In any case, we have a very diverse set of skills, not to mention we had to work without pay in the startup phase. That gave us an impetus to do things a little more rapidly.

"We got lucky in how we ended up with a product that was unique and highly valued. We didn't know anything about oysters until April 2017. We created a plan to produce something special but had to wait about two years to find out if we were going to be successful.

"I think we benefited from the fact that we came into it from backgrounds that had nothing to do with aquaculture or marine science. We didn't have preconceptions.

"We built our own processing equipment. We fabricated our oyster grader according to the industry-standard sizes. It's built out of a pipe and two-by-fours and plywood, and it was intended to be a working prototype. For the first two years, we cranked it

Maine Ocean Farms' boat Cape Anne Diver (Eric Oransky)

by hand until we finally got tired and put a motor on it. We also have another piece of equipment that gives the Wet Smacks their unique handling process and their aesthetic qualities. We just call it the 'R2-T2' unit. It's proprietary."

What are your plans for Maine Ocean Farms?

"Willy and I started a separate business, Casco Marine, two years ago. There was a lot of crossover in our skills because of our commercial marine background. We teamed up with a friend, Zac Pettit, a commercial diver, and an underwater welder. Zac grew up with both of us in the Casco Bay area. Casco Marine creates CAD drawings and engineers and installs mooring systems for aquaculture sites, primarily in the Casco Bay area. When the restaurants closed due to COVID, we were able to pivot and refocus on Casco Marine. That kept us very busy. We were surprised and pleased to see how many new oyster farms are starting up in spite of the uncertainty surrounding everything."

Why do you think that is?

"I think that a lot of folks were locked down at home for months. That led people to reassess what they wanted to do with their lives. A lot of people realized they don't want to spend their lives behind some desk or in a cubicle."

Consulting

"We've also been consulting with some of the state agencies and municipalities associated with aquaculture about improving the review process for mooring systems for aquaculture sites. Many people don't have a technical or engineering background in designing these systems, which must address different loading and dynamic forces than boat moorings. Right now, anybody can draw a mooring plan on paper and submit it as part of their application to the state Department of Marine Resources and Army Corps of Engineers. And if the drawing checks the necessary boxes, it gets approved.

"Then we'd get a mooring plan to install. But we can't install it because the drawings are incomplete. We need to get that application information to people who don't know how to solve

Photo by Bill Perna

these problems simply and safely. If an oyster site starts drifting and gets tangled up in lobster gear and/or with boat lines because the site's gear has not been properly installed, or engineered, that looks bad for our whole industry. This can be a barrier for entry for folks who don't have a technical and engineering background.

Compostable Bags

"Another part of our business at Maine Ocean Farms is selling biodegradable compostable bags for oyster harvesting and distribution. Almost all aquaculture farms and wild-shellfish harvesters use plastic mesh bags. Often the bags only hold the shellfish for a few hours until the restaurant dumps the oysters into a bin to clean them and then serve them. Then they throw out the bags. This is so wasteful. We've developed prototypes.

"These bags are interchangeable with whatever plastic bags people are currently using. There is no retooling or rethinking. Ready-to-use, compostable biodegradable bags. That can eliminate a lot of single-use plastic bags from the waste stream. We are finalizing negotiations to become the U.S. distributor and supplier of these products."

What about climate change, ocean acidification and water warming?

"Yeah, the water is warming in the Gulf of Maine. Warmer water speeds the growth for oysters. For example, oysters around Prince Edward Island might take three or four years to get to market size. In Casco Bay, depending on how you grow them, it can be two to three years to go to market. And you're only talking about a relatively small difference in water temperature. Our water gets up to 72, maybe 74 degrees, in the hottest part of summer. When the water hits the 70-degree mark or just below, we're seeing three millimeters of growth per week on the oysters. With the warming water, we're going to initially see faster growth, which gives us a more rapid return on investment.

"But eventually with the warming comes acidification and oysters are calcifiers. If their water is too acidic, they can't reproduce, or if they do reproduce, they don't have strong enough shells to survive. Acidification worsens as the oceans absorb much of the carbon dioxide that we're putting out through burning fossil fuel.

"There is promising research in multitrophic aquaculture of kelp and/or of other seaweeds or macroalgae that can improve the quality of the water in the immediate vicinity of aquaculture operations.

"There is also concern about the change in ocean currents, in our case the Gulf Stream and Labrador Current, caused by global warming. And there's been a change in the direction of the wind and the frequency of storms."

Opposite: Photo by Aaron Turkel

Love Point Oysters
Founded by Ben Hamilton & Cameron Barner
Casco Bay, Maine

I heard Ben Hamilton speak at a Maine Start-up and New England Ocean Cluster event at Rising Tide Brewery, in Portland. Ben talked about why he wanted to become an oyster farmer. It was an intriguing path for a Yale economics major who had taught English in private schools in Boston and then moved to Maine and joined with business partner Cameron Barner to create Love Point Oysters.

Cameron grew up in Kennebunkport and went to Colby College, and studied environmental studies and biology.

After graduating, he worked as a fisheries observer, or more specifically, an At-Sea Monitor. The ASM program is part of the National Marine Fisheries Service's Northeast Multispecies (groundfish) Management Plan. Cameron would go on fishing vessels on multi-day trips in the Northwest Atlantic, and take data on what was caught and what was discarded. The NMFS would use the data to assess the health of fish populations, so that more accurate quotas could be set for future years.

"While I was interested in aquaculture prior to my job as an observer," he told me, "the destruction of habitat and life, and the inherent wastefulness that I witnessed while observing, drove me to search for a better way to produce our nation's seafood. After learning there was no reality behind the public's glorified perception of 'wild-caught' fish, I knew I wanted to go into aquaculture," Cameron explained to me.

"As one of the newest kids on the block, I am happy to be a part of the conversation," Ben told me. "Love Point Oyster Farm is off the southeast corner of Upper Goose Island, well out into Casco Bay, a lot farther out than a lot of the other farms, which are higher up in the estuaries. We get a lot of salinity and a lot of energy from waves at our oyster farm. There's a lot of water turbulence at our farm. We grow out in floating cages."

After Ben moved to Maine, he said he "immediately gravitated towards starting my own business. I've always had this little bug inside of me telling me to do it, and I knew I wanted to start a business to make the world a better place, and I wanted to work on the water. When I learned the story of farm-raised oyster, I immediately fell in love. This is a virtuous source of protein."

Above: Cameron Barner (left) and Ben Hamilton riding out to farm at sunrise (Mathew Trogner)

Opposite: Courtesy of Love Point Oysters

"That's what's driving me. You know, oysters need zero fertilizer and zero feed. Oysters are pushing the bounds of sustainably produced food, and at the end of the day you get this unbelievably delicious sip of the sea that connects you to the place where it was grown.

"Oysters bring people happiness. Oysters are sustenance. Vitamins, minerals, protein, all that good stuff done in a way that produces no harm to the environment. Growing oysters actually *improves* the environment. It's a source of protein that makes the environment better. That's what lets me look at my three little kids in the eyes and say, 'This is what I do, and this is why I do it.' And you know, it gives me a little motivation to get out there in the mornings and when it's snowing and miserable.

"I didn't know anything about farming before 2017. And I'm a Millennial. So what did I do? I went to Google. I looked up 'How to farm oysters.' It was like a shocking dearth of information. Nothing. The answers weren't there. I had to be very resourceful and talk to other growers. I took a part-time job with Pemaquid Oyster Company. There are amazing organizations in Maine trying to help aquaculture grow: Maine Center for Entrepreneurs, Maine Aquaculture Association, Maine Aquaculture Innovation Center, Darling Marine Center, Maine Sea Grant, Gulf of Maine Research Institute, among others.

"Our primary responsibility as farmers is to not kill oysters. While that sounds rather simple, it turns out that it's really complicated. You have to get deeply connected to nature and understand what's happening with these creatures in your care. And it's very scientific. It's a lot of observations and trying to figure out what's going on. You want to maximize their well-being, make sure they're happy and alive, but this is really

Photo by David Gray

"Working on the water doing oyster aquaculture, you have to work sometimes when the conditions aren't great. But you get to work when they are, so you take the good with the bad. Most of the time I'd much rather be standing on a boat than sitting in an office."

—Ben Hamilton

hard." "And I may have a mortality event in my farm that is totally different from other farmers. So much of this is hands on. Again, you can't Google it. I learned about mortality after my first winter. I bought my seed from Lane Hubacz, of Basket Island Oysters. I'll never forget Lane handing over a bag of oyster babies telling me, 'Here you go, man. Good luck. You're going to need it. You are probably going to kill a lot of oysters. But hang in there, you will figure it out.' I'm like, what does that mean? I thought, I am a smart guy. I'll figure it out.

"Sure enough. You know, when I pulled up an oyster bag after a long winter slumber, it made the sound of a rain stick. … When oysters die and all you are left with is empty shells rolling around in the bag, they make the same pinging sound of the rain sticks that children play with.

"My better half has been telling me, 'My dear husband, keep focused.' But once I finally put myself out there and started this business, every new idea became this beautiful pearl of infinite potential. Everything was like, 'Oh yeah, we're going to do that. That's going to be great. We are going to grow mussels, scallops and kelp. We're going to create an optimism brand and sell more T-shirts. We're going to start an aquaculture festival.' In hindsight, I realized I had wasted a lot of time and should have heeded my better half's advice. I now know I want to grow oysters. I want to be on the water for all the romanticism that is baked into doing this very hard work. And so, yeah, my advice is to pick something, pick one thing, and get really good at it.

"This last challenge, climate change, keeps me up at night. We all face it. The Gulf of Maine is warming faster than 99 percent of the world's oceans. With it comes more frequent intense storms, harmful algae blooms that would result in prolonged harvest closures of shellfish, more acidity, less calcium carbonate, making it harder for shells to form. We are trying to figure this all out, so as I look to the future, I see a great deal of learning and growth."

Thanksgiving Harvest (Mathew Trogner)

Winnegance Oysters
Founded by Jordan Kramer
New Meadows River, Maine

Jordan Kramer grew up in Portland, Maine, and studied biology and environmental science at Vassar College and at the world-famous Marine Biological Laboratory in Woods Hole, Massachusetts. He spent a decade as a biology technician at the Rachel Carson National Wildlife Refuge in Wells, Maine, the Maine Audubon Society, and Bowdoin College before he started Winnegance Oyster Farm, in 2014. I had heard a lot about Jordan from many people before we finally met. I had heard that he was a young, very creative guy and a true innovator. We met at the Forage Market Cafe, in Portland. Jordan is reserved and thoughtful. He has given the interrelationship of environmental challenges, technology, and economics much thought.

He has been working on developing new labor-saving oyster-bag technology and has been happy to open-source and share his concept with the entire international oyster-aquaculture community. He told me that he loved hearing from oyster farmers around the world who had implemented his ideas with success. I pressed him a bit about patenting his technology idea. He felt it didn't seem right because he had been funded by a Northeast Sustainable Agriculture Research and Education grant to develop the idea. So he was happy to share it.

Jordan told me: "I wanted to get involved in aquaculture for the environment. I'd spent so long just measuring things happening to the environment and measuring climate change. I learned I could actually take carbon and nitrogen out of the water by growing things. It seemed like a real direct way to do something good."

"I've heard varied takes on acidification, hanging on whether the bathymetry and currents of the Gulf of Maine will prevent us from getting the real pulse of acidification early as the West Coast is getting it with the upwelling currents.

"There are competing things at play for shellfish aquaculture in Maine. There is acidification, potentially harming hatcheries and wild-shellfish spawning. And there are warming ocean temps that could speed up growth. ... So we could start seeing faster adult oyster growth and other shellfish as long as the water isn't too acidic. Temperature and acidity are working against each other. In the short-run, warmth may have more impact than acidity, but acidity will certainly be an important factor. Warmer

Above: Jordan Kramer (Corey Wildnauer-Haigney)

Opposite: Photo by Jordan Kramer

temperatures may also have some big drawbacks by allowing disease and pests into Maine waters.

"It's going to have to change a lot. There's kind of a gold rush for oysters. That's coming from this third wave of growers. When I started, in 2014, there were only three of us on the New Meadows River and now there's maybe 20.

"I see aquaculture diversifying into other species. Quahogs, scallops, urchins, kelp. People have been working for a long time on multitrophic aquaculture (which is two or more species of organisms grown together). But it hasn't seen a lot of commercial adoption yet."

Right & Following Page: Photos by Jordan Kramer

Long Cove Sea Farm
Founded by Abby Barrows
Long Cove, Maine

Abby Barrows was born and raised in Stonington, Maine. Trained as a marine biologist, she's worked on lobster boats, tall ships, in classrooms and labs. Her mission is to improve water quality and increase access to locally grown sustainable seafood.

In 2015, Abby Barrows and her husband, Ben Jackson, were looking for some oysters to eat and phoned Stonington oyster-farm owner Ginnie Olsen. Ginnie replied, "We don't have any oysters, but do you want to buy the oyster farm?"

"I was surprised that Ginnie wanted to sell it," Abby told me.

So Abby became the owner of Long Cove Sea Farm, which includes 2.45 acres of leased ocean off Long Cove on Deer Isle, where Stonington is.

It took the better part of a year to get through all of the bureaucracy - a real challenge, Abby said. "Transferring the lease was the easier part, but having to get approval from the Army Corps of Engineers and the DMR was tougher. The hardest part was getting the correct licensing for selling oysters."

She brought considerable knowledge of biology to the challenge.

"I have a bachelor of science degree in zoology. I studied at the University of Tasmania. After graduating I went to work as a marine biologist in Papua New Guinea.

"I came back to Maine and worked at the Shaw Institute, in Blue Hill, for a few years. The Shaw Institute is a scientific-research organization based in Maine and New York. It was founded in 1990 by environmental-health scientist Dr. Susan Shaw, and its mission is to discover and expose environmental threats to people and wildlife through innovative science and to engage in global partnerships to improve human and ecological health. I would have guest speakers come in. That's when I first learned about microplastics. I shifted into the research department, where I worked as the coastal water-monitoring coordinator and expanded the microplastic research. Microplastics pose an increasing threat to sea life and other life, too.

"When you are monitoring water, you're looking at the short term, as in what can we do now to improve the quality, as well

Above: Abby Barrows (Jenny Nelson-Wylde Photography)

Opposite: Long Cove Sea Farm from above (Megan Dewey-Wood)

as the long, long view in terms of what may become a problem. I conducted water-quality research at the Maine Environmental Research Institute, which is now the Shaw Institute, and which had monitored water for 10 years. … I was looking at 10 years of data from all the different sites we had monitored in and around Blue Hill Bay, both in the ocean and in freshwater. We saw a clear trend in increasing sea-surface temperatures, even in that short snapshot of time. Our findings echoed findings in the rest of the Gulf of Maine. The Gulf of Maine is warming. That is one of the biggest takeaways.

"That was seven years ago. We also saw some changes in phytoplankton communities. There were different types and frequencies of harmful algal blooms. Some species of phytoplankton were relative newcomers to the Gulf of Maine.

"Toward the end of the 10 years of monitoring, we were seeing an increase of different species in the Gulf of Maine, such as *Pseudo-nitzschia*, which is a marine planktonic responsible for the neurological disorder known as amnesic shellfish poisoning (ASP)," Abby told me.

"You have to remain optimistic. The environment is changing and many species that used to thrive no longer will, but there are some that will weather the changes. Wild-caught fisheries will most likely diminish over time. That's one of the reasons I got into aquaculture. Through traveling and my studies, I became aware of the global fisheries crisis. Many wild commercial populations are in decline, and the demand for seafood is only increasing. We put a lot of pressure on our wild stocks. We have used the ocean like a bank account that we keep drawing from. But we do not put very much back. Things are bottoming out and we see that. It's fairly rare that there's a case of a

well-managed fishery. Looking at the global scale, I recognized that our oceans are in peril on many levels from pollution and overfishing.

"I saw oyster aquaculture in two ways. First, oyster aquaculture is a sustainable fishery. You're actively doing good for the environment. Oysters increase water clarity and water quality. Water clarity increases light penetration, which can help algae and seagrass (such as eelgrass) grow. Vegetation in the water provides habitat and nursery areas for other species. Adult oysters can each filter up to 50 gallons of water in a day. Oyster reefs can help protect the coastline from storm surges as well. The list

Above: Another Foggy One (Abby Barrows)

Opposite: Hibernating Oysters Dreaming of Warmer Days (Abby Barrows)

goes on and on for the environmental benefits of having filter feeders in the ocean. And we know that here in Maine the mussel population has been declining. Oyster aquaculture is a good way to help balance that out.

"Second, I live on this island (Deer Isle). Fishing and having a working waterfront is what defines our culture and our community. The writing is on the wall that change is coming. Fisheries, particularly the lobster fishery, are not going to continue the way they have been.

"I believe there are going to be some big shifts in the next five or 10 years, certainly in my lifetime. My hope is that shellfish aquaculture provides a model for lobstermen or others involved in fisheries. I hope to showcase a viable alternative for people who have spent their life working on the water and help them make a transition when the economics and lobster population changes in Penobscot Bay.

"We don't want to lose what defines and gives strength to our community. Stonington is one of the largest lobster-landing ports in the country. When the industry drops out, how do we redefine our community? You know, there's a lot of people who already have second or third homes here. I don't want Stonington to become only a seasonal island, without any industry except for ice cream and T-shirts.

What's the carrying capacity for oysters in our local environments?

"Carrying capacity is the amount or maximum load of organisms, or crops, that a region can support without environmental degradation. I don't have the answer to this question but

historically there have been large and healthy populations of oysters and other bivalves along the coast. The mussel population has greatly diminished in the last couple of decades and so there is definitely space for more filter feeders. I'd be curious to see what other people in the industry have to say. As humans we tend to overdo everything."

What will the coast of Maine look like in 20 years?

"If aquaculture continues in the current trend there are a lot of pretty interesting dynamics. But there may be pushback here in Vacationland. Many people come here because they want to look out on the ocean, not oyster farms."

She continued, "The idea of aquaculture for some people is it is an eyesore. It's an interesting and often contradictory relationship of people from away who want to have a 'real' Maine Coast experience, but they don't want to smell the bait or hear the boats in the morning, see the gear and equipment. They just want the seafood dinner. There has been a lot of pushback from waterfront owners.

"It's ironic to me that this attitude is a big part of the obstacles that oyster farmers are having to face. Yet I am sure there have been grumblings about lobster buoys when they started to be a common sight, so perhaps it is just an adjustment period of people becoming accustomed to the new landscape - a landscape of sustainable interaction with the ocean."

Opposite: Oyster Cold Storage (Abby Barrows)

Innovation in the Future Blue Economy

Dana Morse
Maine Sea Grant Extension Associate

Dana Morse had years of experience working in shellfish aquaculture and oyster farming in particular. I spoke with Dana via phone after the COVID-19 pandemic started and in person at the Darling Marine Center about where he thinks that the industry is going.

"My work is in three areas, mostly. The first is education: workshops, seminars, meetings and that sort of thing, as well as more formalized programs like Aquaculture in Shared Waters. The Aquaculture in Shared Waters program prepares fishermen to start an aquaculture venture, with associated research to understand the attitudes, perceptions and knowledge of fishermen with respect to this change. The project builds on some very successful and innovative earlier programming by the Maine Aquaculture Association and the Maine Aquaculture Training Institute. These can be for oyster farmers directly, or for other audiences, like consumers, or members of the public interested in the industry. The second is applied research: working with farmers to address some opportunity or problem, such as longline production. The third part is technology transfer: learning about some product or process of interest and seeing what might work here in Maine. An example of that was bringing Rheal Savoie, president of Bouctouche Bay Industries, developer and

Opposite: John Swenson and Dana Morse (David Gray)

designer of the OysterGro system, to Maine several years ago, and organizing workshops at the Northeast Aquaculture Conference and Expo on solar power to power upwelling systems.

"I had a definitely circuitous path," said Dana, who mostly grew up in New Hampshire. "I'm glad I arrived where I did, but it wasn't a straight line. My undergraduate degree was in wildlife management from the University of New Hampshire, but after working in wildlife for a couple of years it was difficult to find steady work. I went to graduate school in the University of Rhode Island's fisheries program and that was for fishing-gear technology."

"I was in Rhode Island for a couple of years. I worked at a couple of different places, including Moonstone Oyster, then owned by Bob Rheault, who has gone on to run the East Coast Shellfish Growers Association. And then I spent almost a year as an aquaculture-gear salesman. I was not much of a salesman. I didn't like the selling part of it, but what I really enjoyed was visiting with farmers and talking about equipment and methods, talking shop anywhere between Eastport, Maine, and Maryland.

"While still in Rhode Island, I was commuting an hour and a half to get to Pocasset, Mass., where I worked on fishing-gear trials with Arne Carr, at the Massachusetts Division of Marine Fisheries. It was good work, but I really didn't want to move to Massachusetts, and the commute was killing me. Plus, I had really enjoyed *part* of the aquaculture-gear sales job and had met several folks who did extension work in aquaculture: Rollie Barnaby (N.H.), Gef Flimlin (N.J.), Gregg Rivara (N.Y.) and Dale Leavitt (Mass.). They looked like they were doing really interesting work, which was very much appreciated both by science and by industry, and they sure looked like they were having a blast. When the position at Maine Sea Grant opened up, I jumped right on it. Getting hired into this job was one of the very best things ever to happen to me, ever."

He noted that because of changes over time in such things as husbandry, equipment and location, "you start to notice different attributes to our oysters" that can be marketed as the sector expands in coming years. "If you look with any kind of critical eye at what an oyster is, you will notice differences in shell shape and texture, the amount of a thin shell at the edge or depth of a cup and all that kind of stuff. Our product offerings will be diversified because even though they're all oysters, they'll have different attributes."

He warned that some of the current social and political challenges will continue, such as "the conflicts that arise every now and then about putting aquaculture sites into Maine's coastal waters."

But then, making decisions about public property *is* complicated. I am a fan of the process that Maine DMR and its partner agencies use, because I think that they set a reasonably high bar for using those public resources, and provide several opportunities for engagement by industry and citizens alike. Nothing's perfect, of course, but it's a pretty solid system.

Right: Courtesy of Little Island Oyster Co.

Dana speculated on possible answers to some NIMBY-like problems:

"The best ways to avoid conflict that I know of are 1: good site selection and 2: communication. You won't always please everyone, but these two things really go a long way.

"Two things along the lines of what I'm thinking, and one is an oyster example and one is not. The non-oyster example is I'm working with a fisherman, Marsden Brewer, in Stonington, on scallops. He is a fisherman and comes from a traditional fishing background. The site that he chose and the way he has laid out his farm and the way he has communicated with other fishermen has been very effective, and it happened that way because he is intimately familiar with the area, and he'd been very careful to talk with the people that fish in the area to describe what he's doing, and to show them.

"So, he is able to conduct his scallop farming while allowing other fishermen to fish through his farm, even though there is a little impact and a little imposition. It's a really good model to show how these activities can co-exist. When you look at it, nobody's really losing anything.

"On oysters, there are a good number of examples of farms that got placed the way they did because the farmers talked to their neighbors on the water and on the adjacent shores. In several cases too -- I'm thinking about the Bagaduce River at the moment -- there are examples where the farmers and the shorefront owners have gone from opponents to supporters of one another. The rules of being a good neighbor very much apply.

"The oyster-related example is in Massachusetts, where there are what are essentially development parks for oyster farms. They're chopped up into little farms. In Japan, scallop cooperatives work in that way."

Dana said that the industry needs to continue "to train new producers and continue professional development for existing producers." And he suggested that farmers will be challenged to keep up prices as more people enter the sector.

He continued: "It's hard to predict what will happen with climate change. Warming waters may benefit oysters, but other species might not benefit, and with a changing climate come changes in water quality. You're already seeing how Mook Sea Farm has had to adapt, by installing equipment and processes that buffer the water coming into their hatchery. The best that my crystal ball allows me to see is that growers should be ready for the unexpected, and that diversification and being nimble will help adapt to those changes. Easier said than done."

In any case, he said, "We need to continue to brand Maine oysters for the really superior product attributes that they have. Maine needs to market more, especially as production, and so competition, from elsewhere increases, both within the United States and outside."

Aquaculture Changing Lives in Georgetown

Aquaculture North America
Matt Jones (2019)

The island community of Georgetown, Maine, has been struggling since the fisheries they've depended on for a living have all but dried up. Pat Burns, a Georgetown resident of more than 30 years, knew something had to be done.

"Our (wild) harvest used to include clams, mussels, finfish, ground fish, lobster, shrimp and even tuna to a certain extent," says Burns. "Lobster is pretty much the only one left. In 2015, our clam harvest was the lowest in 25 years and that was primarily due to the warming of the Gulf of Maine. Green crabs have also begun to invade our watersheds and the clam harvest began to suffer dramatically."

In addition to the environmental issues, the island's population engaged in fisheries is aging. Although some younger people are going into aquaculture, they are the exception rather than the rule. Burns sees oyster aquaculture as a great way to help maintain and restore the marine economy. But he knew that the start-up costs could be prohibitively expensive. Enlisting the help of investor Michael Bonny, Burns used his background in finance to establish Georgetown Aquaculture LLC, in 2016. Bonny splits his time between Massachusetts and Maine. The company aims to kick-start oyster farming on the island by offering farmers financing to help them with startup costs. Within five months, five new oyster farms were born.

"We started the LLC to provide microloans to five farmers

Opposite: Photo by Jordan Kramer

initially, but now we're up to eight farmers. We pledged to fund them for approximately five years at 2 percent, as low an interest rate as we could provide. In the first five years, they're only responsible for repaying at the 2-percent interest rate. At the end of the five years, they will begin to repay the principal plus interest rate. The goal is for them to be completely out of debt at the end of 10 years. By that time, they would be completely independent and owning their own oyster farms." He hopes that by that time, the farmers will also have the capability to finance any expansion.

Unique Funding Model

"This form of financing is into perpetuity. These funds will be paid back into the pool by the current farmers and then re-loaned again to new farmers who perhaps want to raise seaweed or to raise scallops, or to add to the current crop of oyster farmers," Burns told the local paper, The Times Record.

"We are now in a position, with the repayment of the interest on these loans, to be able to fund future farmers for literally forever, or as long as we continue to have the repayment on those loans," Burns tells ANA. "In most philanthropy, it's one off; you really don't see it continuing and going into the future. Ours is a rather unique funding model."

Partnerships with a variety of educational institutions around the state have enabled the company to provide farmers with additional support. Dana Morse, of Maine Sea Grant, has offered workshops to educate farmers to help them avoid beginner mistakes. Most of the farmers are "watermen" – having spent most of their lives on the water, harvesting wild lobster, clams and quahogs – so they have adapted to the industry quickly.

However, there is a certain amount of technical knowledge required to make any aquaculture operation work.

Farmer Ken McIntyre is one of the beneficiaries. "This is something my wife and I thought about getting into for a really long time, but we could never come up with the money to do it. People contributing money into this with a very low interest rate made everything doable. They helped us in every step of the process, from figuring out how many cages we needed to how much seed to buy, to filling out application forms. It really worked out great for us," he says.

"The marine economy is just dwindling here," said farmer Chad Campbell, who has become co-manager of Georgetown Aquaculture. "I've been a wild-shellfish harvester for 20-something years full time and relied on it. Now, you have no choice other than aquaculture if you want to stay in the shellfish business."

The farmers have impressed Burns. He says he now knows all the loan applicants personally and he believes in them. "You could call these character loans more than anything," Burns says. "We're now in our second year of financing and no one has missed a single interest payment to date. Our faith, I think, has been well placed. They have a unique character here. They do not like debt, and they believe in a handshake."

Georgetown Aquaculture sees aquaculture growing on the island. To prepare for this growth, the company applied to reserve 27 acres with the Maine Department of Marine Resources for future farm sites. They were approved for only 14 acres.

"We were disappointed not to get it all," says Burns, who plans

Pat Burns (Greg Rec, Portland Press Herald)

to reapply for additional acreage. "But we're pleased with the roughly 688,000 square feet we currently have. This gives us room for new farms within the next five to 10 years."

Burns says they are also forming a co-op with their farmers and several other independent farmers in the area. Research is also underway on quahog farming, although for now production is focused on oysters based on its return on investment. "One lesson I learned early on was to focus on one effort and succeed in it before venturing into something else. Now that we're going into our third year, we'd very much like to look at quahogs as our next enterprise sometime this year or next."

"Long after I have gone my hope is that this aquafarming will have grown to have a very positive effect not only in the financial aspect of this community but in the cultural adhesion and the interrelationships of the individuals who live here."

Opposite: Man planting Muscongus Oysters (Courtesy of Muscongusbay.com)

"The marine economy is just dwindling here. I've been a wild shellfish harvester for 20-something years full time and relied on it. Now, you have no choice other than aquaculture if you want to stay in the shellfish business."

—Chad Campbell
Co-manager of Georgetown
Aquaculture Co-op

Chris Vonderweidt
Gulf of Maine Research Institute

Chris Vonderweidt runs the aquaculture program at the Gulf of Maine Research Institute. He supervised the creation of the "Maine Farmed Shellfish Analysis" of 2016.

I spoke with Chris at the Gulf of Maine Research Institute, in Portland. "Market performance has exceeded expectations. Incredibly, many growers are getting higher prices today than the average price in the 2017 report, despite continued increases in production. There are fluctuations in price throughout the year. Different people pay different amounts but it's a good price. People are willing to pay a premium for Maine oysters."

"We're approaching the warming of the Gulf of Maine as a threat to Maine's working waterfront heritage and trying to be forward thinking about how Maine's working waterfront can adapt and be preserved. To retain the economic and cultural heritage of people working on the water. The people wearing boots, taking boats to work, shopping at the marine-supply stores. It's an interesting way of life and it's important economically. Aquaculture is a way to adapt to that. So that if a fish becomes less available, if lobster becomes less available to people on the coast of Maine, what are they going to do? They can start a sea farm or work on one."

Right: Courtesy of Glidden Point Oyster Farms

Value of Maine Oysters
Portland Press Herald

The value of Maine's oyster crop has surged as farms have sprung up in recent years. According to state landings data, in 2011 a total of 603,415 pounds of oysters were brought in. By 2017, oyster farmers were hauling in more than four times that number, bringing in nearly 2.8 million pounds.

That growth spurt appeared to taper off in 2018, with 2,762,941 pounds – 33,276 pounds under the previous year – but the total value of the fishery continued to increase, to $7.2 million. And in 2019 Maine's oyster aquaculture produced 13,899,299 oysters, for a value of $9,670,100.

That's quite a change when you consider that from 2004 to 2011, the total landed value of Maine's oyster fishery fluctuated between $1 million to $2 million annually.

That figure refers only to the value of the oysters landed. When considering all the associated businesses that support and rely on the oyster harvest, its economic impact would increase dramatically to $13.6 million in 2018, said Chris Davis, the executive director of the Maine Aquaculture Innovation Center.

To meet demand, a 2016 analysis published by the Gulf of Maine Research Institute called for the total amount of acreage devoted to shellfish aquaculture to double by 2030. While that's a significant push, under those projections shellfish aquaculture would use just 0.1 percent of the state's coastal waters. In 2016, shellfish leases covered 0.06 percent of the waters.

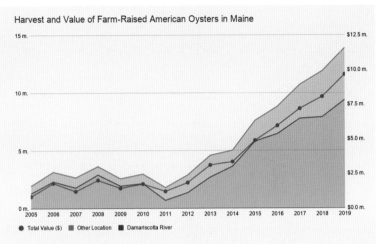

Harvest and Value of Farm-Raised American Oysters in Maine

● Total Value ($) ■ Other Location ■ Damariscotta River

Source: Maine Department of Marine Resources

That analysis projected that Maine oyster production would almost triple by 2030. A higher estimate shows production nearly quadrupling. For that to happen, Maine's coastal waters devoted to aquaculture obviously need to be substantially increased.

MURIEL HENDRIX EXCERPTS

The following excerpts give valuable insight and historical context. Muriel's articles about Maine's aquaculture were originally published in Working Waterfront. They can now be found in the book Unlimited Ingenuity and Industrious Entrepreneurs: Stories of Aquaculture in Maine, 1998-2016, *published by the Maine Aquaculture Innovation Center.*

"NIMBY Makes a U-Turn"
Working Waterfront (2009)

Brooksville, Maine, resident Anne Bossi, with the help of her many goats, runs Sunset Acres Farm, a saltwater farm on the shores of the Bagaduce River, in Penobscot County. She and her husband, Bob Bowen, produce some of the most awarded artisanal cheeses in Maine. Anne was concerned about Jesse Leach's application for a lease to raise oysters in the Bagaduce River close to her farm's shoreline. Like many people faced with the prospect of an aquaculture lease in their backyards, she was afraid that the venture would disturb the environment of the quiet, pristine river she had prized for 10 years and might cause a drop in property value.

"For 10 years, I'd seen nothing but water and birds," she says. "I was not anxious to look out and see whatever it was I was going to see. I wasn't sure what that would be, what noise or activity level." She was so upset by the prospect that she even tried to

Opposite: Bagaduce River (Maine Nature Conservancy)

lease the river bottom herself. She learned that no one's allowed to lease the bottom unless it is to be farmed.

Bossi says a combination of factors caused her to have a change of heart. "First off," she says, "there was no choice. It was a done deal." She added: "Jesse has been very nice to work with. I began to recognize that oyster production is not that objectionable. After all, we're both farmers." She admits that after Jesse's oyster-lease hearing she felt guilty about objecting.

Originally from Cape Cod, she didn't want to be like other people who "come from away" and want to recreate the place they left, get rid of the noise, the early-rising lobstermen, the odor of bait and the traps in the yard. Now, she and Leach can sit at her kitchen table and talk about the many problems they have in common as farmers. Both have to deal with a mountain of rules and regulations. Bowen delivers cheese to 24 stops every Wednesday and they go to four different farmers' markets each week. Leach says he sells 98 percent of his oysters to wholesalers, who send them out of state, but he would also like to sell at local farmers' markets.

Both talk about managing production to keep customers supplied year-round, and they mention other crops and animals they have raised and the continuous need to adapt to current markets and remain diverse enough to make a living as markets change.

Bossi says that the first concession she asked of Leach was to preserve her favorite view. "I took Jesse into the house," she says, "and dragged him over to the kitchen sink. 'Jesse,' I said, 'I love this view. I'd be happy if you could keep it clear of buoys and floating things.'"

A year or two after he started using his lease, Leach realized that he needed electricity to run upweller pumps that would pull a stronger flow of water from the bottom, that tidal flow wasn't enough. "I'd been using tidal flow to bring nutrients to the seed. Upwellers are where pin-sized baby oysters grow to the size for grow-out bags that float on the water." He asked for permission to tap into the farm's electrical supply. Baby oysters are raised in upwellers. They have electric motors that increase the water flow for the baby oysters. Bossi and Bowen said "sure" and put in a pole that Leach paid for, as well as a separate meter for the line he ran to the shore.

Leach also asked if he could run a freshwater line from their supply to clean algae from the mesh bags. Bossi and Bowen said no problem. Leach said that they have helped in other ways, such as letting him put his floats up on their land in the winter rather than take them home. "They've been wonderful," he said of the couple.

Leach usually accesses his site from the town landing at the bridge upriver but uses a strip of land on the farm property to store some gear and attach a float. At first, he and Bossi agreed that he would pay for this use. It wasn't long until they turned to bartering. Leach has helped put up a greenhouse, build fences and dig out some hay. He encourages Bossi and Bowen to use his float, and if they develop a yen for some oysters, a bag will be hanging there for them.

Bossi believes that if she had known more about the actual operation of an oyster farm she would not have been as apprehensive about Leach's application for a lease. "I'd say to any riparian owner that it would be a good idea to see photos of different operations, get to know what's involved as far as noise and disruption. Everyone wants the water to be pristine, but a working waterfront is a good thing. It's a way of life here."

Meanwhile, she has discovered that Leach's farm may have an unanticipated value. "A neighbor a couple of places downriver is a Maine Guide," she says. "I heard his plan was to have a seaplane on the river to use to take clients up to the North Woods. I thought, 'Oh my God, I hope Jesse's oyster farm prevents that.'"

Courtesy of Glidden Point Oyster Farms

"Oyster Aquaculture Has Come a Long Way"
Working Waterfront (2004)

The industry had to go through years of experimenting with new techniques for hatchery culture, and nursery and grow-out methods, before this became possible. Early researchers and farmers tried out oddly shaped floating nurseries made of wood, plastic and various types of screening; stacked grow-out trays, trays planted on the bottom, and oysters planted loose on the bottom. Finally, most settled (for a while, at least, and with several variations) on a combination of surface and bottom cultures. They used floating oyster bags in the early stages and planted oysters directly on the bottom for final grow-out. "We always joke about the technology graveyard – all the stuff we've gone through," says Carter Newell, of Pemaquid Oysters. "We've struggled for so long."

The earliest wave of growers focused on the European, or Belon, oyster, *Ostrea edulis*, which in the early days sold for around 50 cents each while the American, or Eastern oyster, *Crassostrea virginica*, brought only 15 or 20 cents apiece. In the late 1970s, when a winter die-off killed 90 percent of the European oyster crop, almost all of the early growers decided to move on to other ventures, and a new wave of oyster farmers came on the scene, some of them people who had done graduate work with Herb Hidu.

In the early days of oyster aquaculture, growers built much of their equipment out of materials they scrounged or bought at hardware and department stores. Many still do this, although commercial equipment is now available. Chris Davis, an original partner in Pemaquid Oysters, says that for about 15 years Pemaquid Oysters used homemade wooden nursery trays built of hackmatack with window screening held on by oak lathes. "They weighed 15 pounds dry and about 60 pounds when they were waterlogged, fouled with marine animals and plants, and full of oysters," he says. Pulling them out for cleaning (fouling would clog the mesh and prevent water from circulating freely through the trays to bring phytoplankton to the oysters) was backbreaking.

THE EATING SECTION

Bon Appétit selected Portland, Maine, as its national "Restaurant City of the Year, 2018." But besides such famous Portland farm-to-table and sea-to-table restaurants as Fore Street and Hugo's, there's a wealth of such innovative Maine farm-to-table restaurants as Primo, in Rockport, not to mention all of the "lobster shacks" up and down the coast and such suppliers as Harbor Fish and Browne Trading, in Portland.

Travelers have long loved Maine's 3,478 miles of craggy coastline, pine trees, lighthouses and lobsters from cold, clean waters. In the 1930s someone made the brilliant decision to put "Vacationland" on Maine license plates and to marry the idea of "Maine" to lobster.

The term "merroir," ("of the sea") recalls the French word "terroir" ("of the earth"), which describes how certain foods and wine bear the flavors of their home soil and climate. The environment in which a particular wine is produced, including such factors as soil, topography and climate, create the characteristic taste imparted to it.

The merroir includes such variables as growing methods and environment that contribute to the differences among oysters.

Indeed, oysters aren't that different from wines insofar as they are site-expressive, meaning that their taste is shaped by the

Opposite: Harbor Fish Market in Portland, Maine (Courtesy of Harbor Fish Market)

characteristics of their growing environment. Water salinity, temperature, the type of algae present in the water and seabed characteristics all factor into an oyster's flavor.

Julie Qiu, who is based in Brooklyn, is the founder of the oyster blog In a Half Shell and co-founder of Oyster Master Guild. Julie and Catherine Schmitt were instrumental in helping Maine Sea Grant develop the Maine Oyster Trail concept.

Julie Qiu told me: "As an international oyster fanatic, I find it wise to be diplomatic when I'm asked where the best oysters come from by telling the asker to remember that every oyster-producing region can grow exceptional oysters. I can rave over an oyster from anywhere, as long as it's served in peak condition.

"But I've got a confession: I secretly favor Maine oysters over all other regions in North America. Maybe I'm biased from happy childhood memories of Acadia National Park and romantic summer trips with my then-boyfriend, now husband. Maine has always served us well as a place of relaxation and renewal. We even got married in Stockton Springs and toasted our new life together with champagne and local oysters. Objectively speaking, I think the pristine environment and bracingly cold waters of the Gulf of Maine make the oysters here taste a cut above the rest."

Oyster Trail of Maine

The first concept of the Maine Oyster Trail, originally called the

Oyster Trail of Maine, was developed by Maine Sea Grant in collaboration with the Maine Aquaculture Association and the Maine Aquaculture Innovation Center in 2017. The original Trail was designed to give consumers a window into the world of Maine's oyster industry by directing them to locations where they could tour farms and buy oysters. This was achieved through a map of Maine's oyster farms and a list of restaurants and fish markets that sell the state's oysters. The mission was also to educate consumers about the more scientific aspects of Maine oyster aquaculture.

The 2020 coronavirus pandemic and associated closure of most of the restaurant market dealt an enormous blow to Maine's oyster industry. To adapt to the pandemic, many oyster farmers began to incorporate direct-to-consumer sales and farm tours into their revenue streams.

For Heather Sadusky and Jaclyn Robidoux (Maine Sea Grant), these adaptations sparked an idea. In August 2020, they approached Afton Hupper, Outreach & Development Specialist at Maine Aquaculture Association, about revamping the trail. Together, the women rebranded the Oyster Trail of Maine as The Maine Oyster Trail, and transformed it into an interactive guide designed to help visitors plan oyster experiences that are uniquely Maine.

The new Maine Oyster Trail (to be launched in 2021) will direct visitors to oyster-farm tours and special events, farm stands, raw bars, shucking lessons and opportunities to buy oysters directly from farmers. The Trail will also feature a "digital passport" trip planner and verification codes for participants to collect rewards as they check in to locations along the Trail. The Trail will help people looking for socially distanced activities during

this unprecedented time connect to these new opportunities and explore what their own communities and state have to offer.

The number of individual oyster farms in Maine has been increasing in recent years, with now more than 150 farms from Ogunquit to Corea. "We expect at least 50 oyster farms up and down the coast to become part of the Trail in 2021," says Afton Hupper. As Heather Sadusky explains: "The idea is to generate revenue for Maine oyster farmers through tours and direct sales, as well as educate consumers about the social, ecological and economic benefits of aquaculture on the coast of Maine." Further, the Trail will "provide unique and unforgettable experiences to curious visitors from near and far, and help consumers connect directly with growers to learn more about where their seafood comes from," says Jaclyn Robidoux. Stay tuned for the 2021 launch of the Maine Oyster Trail.

When I asked a Maine oyster farmer how she liked her oysters, she said: "I prefer my oysters sold."

what side of the hill in Burgundy grapes are grown will have a really big impact on the wine you are making.

"I learned just how intensely oysters are reflective of and depend on their environment. On my farm, Nonesuch Oysters, in Scarborough, Maine, we have seven small acres. Oysters even more than grapes are a reflection of where they are from."

"An oyster is the perfect embodiment of where it's grown."

—*Abigail Carroll*

Nonesuch Oysters
Scarborough, Maine
Abigail Carroll

"Every single oyster from Canada all the way down the East Coast and into the Gulf of Mexico, with only one exception that I am aware of, which is the Belon (European) oyster, is the exact same species of oyster, the *Crassostrea virginica*, which is the American or Eastern oyster," Abigail noted to me.

"So, what makes them taste different? The local growing environment. Like wine in the *terroir*.

"Chardonnay grapes from California will make very different Chardonnay wine from one made in Burgundy, France. Even

Above: Abigail Carroll, Nonesuch Oysters, and Julie Qiu, of the blog In a Half Shell. (Alexander Krieckhaus)

Eventide
Portland, Maine
Mike Wylie

Mike Wiley and I met at 3 o'clock on a Friday afternoon at Eventide, one of Portland's popular oyster-serving restaurants. I had assumed that he picked that time because it wouldn't be too busy. But when I arrived I found that the place was packed with customers. I was led through a very busy kitchen to meet Mike at his adjoining restaurant, Hugo's. Hugo's opened, in 1988, as a humble family eatery. It has gone on to gain national recognition for its refined cuisine. The kitchen staff seemed to be rushing to get ready for the big evening show.

Above: Courtesy of Eventide

Mike told me about his multi-restaurant company, Big Tree Hospitality.

"I have two business partners, Arlin Smith and Andrew Taylor. We own and operate Hugo's. We're the third owners of the restaurant. We opened Eventide Oyster Restaurant in the adjoining space next door in 2012, and in 2015 the Honeypaw Restaurant, which is just next door to Eventide. In 2017, we opened Eventide Fenway, in Boston's Fenway neighborhood.

"I got into cooking from ski bumming and rock climbing out West. It was a great way to pay the bills. You'd knock back a couple of beers with the guys after a shift, go to bed too late and get up too early and ski your brains out and then just snack on restaurant food the entire shift and do it all over again.

"Then I got kind of shown a little more of the artistic side of cooking professionally at Le Bosquet, in Crested Butte, Colorado, and I really started to enjoy that. I was living out there then and I really wanted to have a little more intellectual rigor in my life and I come from a long line of dorks. My father was an anesthesiologist, my mother an English professor, and I always thought I'm going to end up in academia at some point. School came easy and I always got praise for my writing. So, I thought, hey, that's a career path. But after getting my master's in rhetoric at the University of Colorado, it became abundantly clear that academia was not for me.

"I was longing for the days of oven burns and cleaning up fryolator spills. So, I got back into working in kitchens as soon as I could. I moved back to Maine. I was born in Portland and had graduated from Colby College.

"I wrote a really pompous cover letter in an application for a job as a fish cook at Hugo's Restaurant. I talked about how I had longed to return to Maine and once again wear flannel proudly, yada, yada, yada. And despite the pomposity I was hired and then made the sous chef shortly thereafter. That's where I met Andrew and Arlin, my two business partners, and Rob Evans and Nancy Pugh, the previous owners of Hugo's and now the current owners of Duck Fat Restaurant, here in Portland.

"Rob and Nancy told me they were looking to sell Hugo's Restaurant. They asked me if I'd be willing to write an ad to sell the restaurant I was just hired at. Needless to say, I was taken aback, but Andrew, Arlin and I got to talking and we formed Big Tree Hospitality and bought Hugo's from Rob and Nancy. We also realized that the space right next door was going to become available and we would have a chance at building out a restaurant next door to Hugo's. It would be a little less high concept, a little lower price tag, something akin to Duck Fat in Portland, which is a small European-style cafe known for its duck-fat Belgian fries and milkshakes. We realized that was a really good formula for Rob and Nancy. Unbeknownst to us, we were opening an oyster bar in Portland just as Maine's reputation culturally was skyrocketing and the eating of oysters was enjoying a major renaissance.

"We were outgunned from the get-go. We were very, very busy, and got very little sleep for the first couple of years. Eventide needs lots of space, lots of prep cooks, lots of labor going into the food. They're breaking down lots of lobsters. It is a messy endeavor. And so we just needed more and more space. And our landlord found out we were looking for a commissary kitchen space and said, 'Why don't you guys take the space next door to Eventide? The Pepper Club Restaurant is ending their run.' And we said, 'Sure.' You can't just have lots of lavish kitchen space and justify the rent. You need to open another restaurant. So, we opened the Honey Paw, a bistro that offers Asian-inspired noodles and other things with local craft beer with the aim that it wouldn't compete with Hugo's or with Eventide in terms of style of customer preferences, and I feel like Honey Paw has really hit its stride in the last couple of years.

"From what I see in the dining room at Eventide, enthusiasm for oysters is growing. I don't think we have just a bubble.

"With oysters, we're slowly seeing this kind of trickling down where the people are. It's not just the billionaire class who are interested in having foie gras these days. Young hip diners want to eat that sort of thing. They're interested in matsutake mushrooms. People are broadening their horizons. Maine oysters are a big part of that. There are probably five people today that came into Eventide who just had their first raw oyster. For some people, raw oysters are kind of scary but I think that there's more of an appetite for adventurous dining these days. People care a lot more about their food, where it comes from.

"There's interesting stories and lore behind them. People get pretty excited to hear the phrase 'Maine oysters.' I think about the Maine ecosystem that makes oysters excellent up here and the industry resilient.

"Our oyster listings are half from away, half from Maine. Oysters had gotten expensive for a while. We like to charge a flat rate for oysters. We don't want our Glidden Point Oysters to be less expensive than our Winter Points. We don't want our customers doing math. We want them to order oysters and we'll take care of the rest. Recently we've seen oyster prices coming down just because the market feels flooded. So I think if there's one bad thing from the aquaculture perspective, it's there's a lot of competition. But if that means more people are coming to Maine and having an amazing oyster-eating experience that's fine.

"We are a direct beneficiary of Maine food tourism. Eventide and our other restaurants represent the second culinary renaissance here in Portland. The first being Rob Evans and Sam Heywerd at Fore Street. No doubt that has a lot to do with people who want that merroir or terroir experience and tasting something that was pulled from the water very recently.

"People come into Eventide primed for this incredible Maine oyster experience. As a chef what could be easier than opening an oyster, not hurting yourself, not bursting the belly and getting it in front of the person. That's it. People want that immediacy. It is an appreciation of Maine's naturalness and purity. They see that the oysters are right there, that the person who's growing the blueberries is right there and everybody cooks.

"Maine is also beginning to have great dairies in Maine that are making very good cheeses. I think that some of it just comes from a place where the summers are more temperate and beautiful than in, say, Washington, D.C. Why wouldn't you want to come up here? What a surprise that the waters are less polluted. It stands to reason that filter feeders growing in the waters would taste richer and brinier here in Maine."

"The oyster embodies so much of what people are looking for when they come to Maine to have a Maine experience, culinary or otherwise."

—*Mike Wiley*

"People crave this kind of opportunity, this kind of life experience. Oyster farming is the American dream. It's entrepreneurial. It's creative. The passion is authentic. It's bootstrapping. It's startup."

Maine Oyster Company
Portland, Maine
John Herrigel

"This industry that we're in has exploded at this moment. And we don't know where it is going to go. There is this massive environmental component. There is also this economic component and our lobsters are migrating north. There are all these new oyster farms coming online. Maine has a great brand. So, what am I trying to do? What are we trying to do?

"There's a lot of passion in this industry," John told me. "The more we can keep working together and share together the better. It's just a huge opportunity for us.

Above: Courtesy of Maine Oyster Company

Upstream Trucking
Portland, Maine
George Parr

George Parr has been in the seafood business for four decades and among those who have been instrumental in creating the reputation of Maine oysters. He doesn't hesitate to take a firm stand when buyers "From Away" come to Maine and try to drive down oyster prices rather than pay a fair price for what many consider to be among the world's best oysters. His sense of fairness has benefited not just his clients but all of Maine's oyster growers.

He, like his partner Dana Street, has also been a significant influence in creating Portland's well-deserved reputation as

Above: Courtesy of George Parr

one of the best food towns in the U.S. Dana Street also owns a prestigious portfolio of some of Portland's best restaurants - Street and Company; Fore Street, with Sam Hayward; Standard Bakery, with Alison Pray, and the Scales Restaurant, on the Maine Wharf next to Upstream Trucking. Upstream Trucking is a seafood-wholesaling business that George runs. That's where I met George.

To say that the candid, funny, and direct George, who came to Maine from New York City, is an interesting character would be an understatement. When I met with him he was wearing suspenders, round sunglasses and a well-worn fedora.

One quickly realizes that he understands exactly what it means to be a fishmonger in Portland. He has encyclopedic knowledge that he easily draws from. George has probably forgotten more than many people know about the business. That's a reason he finds himself in the enviable position of being able to turn down business. He has the best restaurant accounts on the Portland peninsula.

"I've been in the fish business for over 40 years. I started in Washington, D.C., as a production cutter at Giant Foods, a big supermarket chain in that area. Then I was in New York, in the old Fulton Fish Market, under the Brooklyn Bridge. After that, I worked for Epicurean International, which represented the Iranian caviar cartel, until 1985.

"I had been selling a lot of salmon roe to the Japanese. A Japanese company, Alaska Suisan, picked me up and in 1988 sent me up here to Maine as a sea-urchin buyer for the Japanese market. I bought 60 million pounds of sea urchins in 10 years that we shipped out of Maine. I had buying stations all along the coast.

That all ended for two reasons. We had exhausted the resource despite my efforts in Augusta (the state capital) to lobby for regulations to avoid over-harvesting, and the Japanese economy flattened.

"After that, I knew I didn't want to go back to New York. That's when Dana Street and I set up this seafood business, Upstream Trucking. We started out just selling to Fore Street Restaurant, Street & Co., and a couple of other accounts around town. I was doing it all by myself. I'd drive down to Boston at four o'clock in the morning two days a week and get done at five or six in the evening. The other days I was getting orders out, and I was basically on call seven days a week. Still am.

"I buy in Boston because it's a logistical hub that brings in products from all over the world. I buy here in Portland as well, for local catch. I started picking up accounts and they started coming to me. I started getting a pretty good reputation. I sell to Eventide Restaurant 3,000 or more oysters a week, and Scales Restaurant and Fore Street a thousand oysters a week each. I became a player in the oyster business.

"Other buyers would always ask me: 'Can we get the price down? This is a huge price bubble here in Maine. And you're part of the problem.' "And I'd say. 'No, you're wrong. The demand is very strong.'

"Every time I turn around, there's somebody coming up to Maine biting at my haunches. I need great oysters to take care of my accounts. These are the premium-priced oysters in North America. And there's a good reason for it. They're exceptional. Some of these oysters are like fine white wines. They all have a unique flavor that comes from where they were grown.

"I started out selling the oysters of just two to three oyster farms. And now I deal with 12 farms, all in Maine.

"I've got all these oyster farmers out there that want to sell to me. But the deal is that if they sell directly to my accounts, I'm not going to buy from them. I used to buy from a farmer who told me, 'I'm going to start selling directly to Eventide.' 'Okay,' I responded, 'you are going to sell directly to my accounts? Okay, I'll see you later.' I had guaranteed them that I would buy a thousand oysters a week. That was a pretty good deal. Now Eventide (a well-known and popular Portland restaurant) maybe buys 200 or 300 oysters a week from them.

"Some Maine growers will sell their oysters to the Grand Central Oyster Bar, in New York, for 65 cents each. Grand Central Oyster won't pay any more than 65 cents. I won't talk to them because they just try to beat me up on price. I came out of New York. I'm pretty immune to the New York attitude. But there are Maine oyster farmers who will ship to the Grand Central Oyster Bar because they want to have their oysters listed on its menu board. I don't think that it does them as much good as they think.

"I've worked with a lot of oyster farmers who were just starting out, such as Mark Green, of Basket Island Oysters, on Casco Bay. When Mark started out, he had a lot to learn. I helped his farm a bit. These are fast learners. They sink the oysters and grow them slower to get a lot better flavor and a lot sturdier shell. Now Basket Island grows one of the best oysters out there.

"Growing slow is superior because oysters need to pick up

minerals for the shell quality. If they're sitting on the surface, they grow really fast, which is why some oyster farmers like to grow them on the surface. But the shells are thin and brittle and the meat is not picking up enough flavor.

"Basket Island Oysters can take up to four years to grow their oysters. They're deep-water oysters. They taste phenomenal. Oysters grown in brackish water do not give you that good, briny flavor. Oysters are like plants. You put an oyster in one location, and it doesn't do well; you put the same oyster in another place, and it thrives. That's why there are a lot of oyster farms on the Damariscotta. The Damariscotta has that huge plankton flow coming in and out every day from the Great Salt Pond.

"I sell other stuff besides oysters. I've sold 80 bluefin tuna since the First of June. All in Portland. It's pretty amazing. I'm dealing with Annie Tselkis, at Casco Bay Seafoods. They move all their bluefin through my warehouse. A lot of their bluefin is export-grade fish. That tuna would be getting a lot more money any other time, but they can't ship them anywhere during COVID.

"When COVID came down, Annie went out and got three boats together. She got her federal tuna buyer's permit and she came to me and asked: 'Can we bring our fish through your building?'

"I said 'Only one fish at a time. I don't want to have a whole bunch of fish stacked up in my walk-in cooler.' George then laughed.

"I think I have five bluefin tuna in my cooler right now. They go out as fast as they come in; they just fly out the door. I know where all the bluefin tuna are going but I can't believe how fast they go out. The Portland chefs have never seen this quality of fish. Last year I was paying top dollar to get top-grade tunas and they still wouldn't give it to me. The fishermen wanted to gamble and send it into Tokyo or New York or LA thinking they're going to get the big bucks, but they never did. So now I'm getting export-grade fish and all the chefs in Portland can't believe the quality of fish they're getting now. They've never seen anything like it. These tuna fishermen catch a 500-pound clunker and they cut it loose. They don't want a 500-pound fish. It doesn't have any fat. I want her like 250-to-350 pound fish.

"There are so many fish out there in the Gulf of Maine. The tuna fishermen can pick and choose which fish. It's crazy. I mean, some people would go out there for years and never catch a fish. These guys go out there for like six hours and come back with a fish. ICCAT, the International Commission for the Conservation of Atlantic Tunas, ended a lot of unsustainable fishing practices, like purse seining, that were driving down the numbers of fish. In the past 30 years or so, the population has dramatically rebounded."

What's Upstream Trucking's future?

"We're doing more out-of-state shipping. All my accounts have been on the Portland peninsula. I have all the best accounts. We are doing more shipping into New York and Boston. But there's only so much Upstream can grow because we're in Portland. It's hard for us to compete with Gloucester and New Bedford. It's like this guy from Boston's North Shore. He says Portland prices are a bubble. Everything is so expensive. It is. But it is also the best quality. Maine has the best quality on the Eastern Seaboard. I hate buying food from New Bedford and Gloucester. Why? Cause it's all terrible. They still unload fish with pitchforks. You get these fish and there are pitchfork holes in the fish."

What's happening with the direct-to-consumer sector?

"It exploded because nobody wants to go to the store people during the thick of COVID."

Who loses in direct to consumer?

"A lot of retail guys. What happened is a lot of retail stores were shutting down at the time due to COVID and then people would start to go online. Now the retail stores have opened back up but the quality of the product that customers get online is five times the quality they were used to at the local seafood store in, say, Cincinnati or Kansas City. I mean they never get good fish. So now they're getting top-shelf fish delivered right to their door. But they are paying top-shelf prices. I deal with a guy here in Portland, who set up a whole direct-to-consumer business in Asian communities across the country. He's selling two-pound chunks of Toro, aka tuna belly, the premium cut of tuna for sushi, for $50 per pound. And then he beats me up on the price. I'm selling him, Toro, for $11 per pound. I said to him 'Seriously. Are you really going to try to beat me up on the price?' I just laughed."

Some of the biggest challenges for Maine oyster aquaculture?

"The biggest problem is that there are too many oyster farmers. There will come a day when their prices are going to go down. I don't know when it will be. I thought that when COVID hit, the prices were going to go down, but it was just a blip. And then all the restaurants started doing curbside and outdoor seating. They're keeping the demand up. I have some restaurants that are doing as much business or more than pre-COVID. You go to Eventide, they have more seats outside than they had inside. So does Duck Fat. Eventide is probably on par with what they were doing last year. Maybe a little less. That's a lot more work doing all this outdoor stuff; you have more overhead. A lot of people didn't survive. Is it the ones who went all-in on curbside and outdoor who are surviving? Unfortunately, Drifters Wife, for example, went out of business, and they're really talented people."

What will happen in the winter when sidewalk dining goes away?

"What will happen in the winter is the million-dollar question. Right now occupancy inside is limited to 50 percent. You get that first drop in temperature and think 'uh-oh.' We'll see what happens to everybody -- from owners and chefs to customers, wholesalers, distributors, farmers, fishermen, the Portland Fish Exchange -- who are vested in keeping the Portland restaurant culture thriving."

Did COVID cause that closing?

"Oh, yeah. Remember, Drifters Wife was on Bon Appetit's list of Best New Restaurants, and they were also named one of the hottest restaurants in the United States. Chef Ben Jackson was nominated as a finalist for the James Beard Award 'Best Chef: Northeast.' And it just breaks my heart they closed.

"A lot of these guys tried to do curbside or takeout when COVID came down. When they started they were losing money. But the ones who stuck with it actually did very well. Some did really well.

"But some Portland restaurants can't get relief from their landlords and it's forcing some to shut down.

"There's nothing they could do. So when the COVID closure came down March 15th, I just was crying. I've worked 20 years building this business and I just saw it all just dissolving in front of me. And it was like a month and a half before I really got the wheels back on the truck and started moving again. And now I'm probably down only about 5 percent from last year. I'm very happily surprised by how much business we are doing.

"When COVID broke out I just sat down and suddenly broke into tears. And my wife says, 'You are grieving.' Afterward, she said that it just clicked for me. I got back on track. Not just for me, for all the businesses that were going to take a hit.

"It was just the three of us, me, my Number 2 and general manager, Rick Humphrey, and Andy Whittaker, who manages the floor for a month and a half. And then finally we're working like 10 hours a day and then coming home and collapsing. And then we started bringing the crew back. I didn't ship up to Boston until the First of May. But now I fill an 18-foot box truck. It's getting to the point where I'm feeling good again."

What makes the best oyster?

"My preference is for deep-water oysters. I don't think brackish water oysters are where it's at.

"There are all kinds of sweet spots in Casco Bay, some protected by islands down here in Portland, others up near Harpswell. The Damariscotta is an estuary but there are also farms down near the mouth which are offshore. There are farms up in Penobscot Bay, too, but I'm limiting my area from about North Haven down to Portland."

Cull & Pistol
New York City
David Seigal

In 1974, the MacGregor family began selling live Maine lobsters to New York restaurants and local residents out of a tiny Upper West Side storefront. In 1995, the business became an original tenant of the iconic Chelsea Market, expanding its product line to include all seafood, and establishing a proper retail store and a sushi bar. Today, the family's company, The Lobster Place, is a full-fledged wholesaler, retailer and hospitality operation, employing over 250 people in its locations in Manhattan and the Bronx.

David Seigal has expanded his menu of Maine oysters to include

Above: Executive Chef David Seigal (Courtesy of Cull & Pistol)

those from 30 farms. David's culinary experience spans almost two decades, during which he worked with acclaimed chefs Charlie Palmer, Jean-Georges Vongerichten, Gray Kunz and David Bouley. He has also worked at the three-Michelin-star Martin Berasategui, in Lasarte-Oria, Spain, and El Raco D'en Freixa, in Barcelona, and Hotel Lenkerhof, in Switzerland. David returned to New York in 2013 and joined the Lobster Place to open Cull & Pistol Oyster Bar in the heart of New York.

"I love Maine oysters," he said. "Customers' reaction to Maine oysters is overwhelmingly positive but I've found that a lot of people are not yet aware that the Maine oyster business is as robust as it is. We generally have about a third of our list from Maine at any given time, and once folks try these oysters they are super-pumped about the experience. Recently the Mere Point oysters were our top seller."

David told me: "Maine's cold waters and the massive tidal swings of its coastal rivers are keys to its oysters' flavor and texture. In addition, that Maine is less populated than states to its south means there tends to be less coastal runoff."

He added, "There are many hard-working Mainers who are deeply passionate about bringing superb oysters to market. They don't rush their products to market, so their oysters tend to be larger, meatier and saltier than those from elsewhere. That's the way I like them."

"The biological characteristics specific to the Damariscotta River make those oysters among my favorites. There are also some great oysters coming out of the New Meadows River and around Casco Bay, as well."

Grand Central Oyster Bar
New York City
Sandy Ingber

Affectionately called "The Bishop of Bivalves," Sandy Ingber trained at the Culinary Institute of the America and has been the executive chef at New York City's most famous seafood institution, the Grand Central Oyster Bar, for 26 years.

The Oyster Bar opened its doors in Grand Central in 1913, when Woodrow Wilson was president.

It was fun to speak with Sandy. He is a very busy man, pulled in

Above: The famed Grand Central Oyster Bar, designed by Spanish architect Rafael Guastavino and his son, Rafael Guastavino Jr., has been very popular since its opening, in 1913. Note the glorious vaulted ceilings. (Courtesy of Grand Central Oyster Bar)

many directions as he runs what may well be the world's foremost oyster bar. He loves oysters, especially Maine oysters.

I asked Sandy how well Maine oysters sold.

"I have 25 oysters on my menu. And I'll usually have two or three Maine oysters. They sell very well. And their sales are growing. Right now, we have Pemaquid, Mere Point, Nonesuch. We also have Belons from the Damariscotta River. Belons are among my favorites. The Mere Points are very good and are selling like crazy.

"Maine oysters are very briny. People who like briny oysters will stick with brine. If they can't get Maine oysters, they will buy oysters from Cape Cod, Rhode Island, New Brunswick.

"Half of our customers are real oyster aficionados who know what they like. The other half will go with recommendations.

"The Belons are Number 1 in the house. That is what we call a true expert oyster eaters' oyster because of its good flavor profile, and it is grown wild.

"I started working at the Oyster Bar in 1990 and we sold Pemaquid Oysters using the name Pemaquid. They didn't sell very well. Then they changed the name from Pemaquid to calling them Americans. But nobody wanted an oyster called an American, so we changed the name again and called them Bristols. Bristol is on the Damariscotta River and the oysters would sell. Now fast forward to the late '90s, and for some reason the name Pemaquid began to circulate all over New York City. And when I saw that, I put the name Pemaquid Oysters back on my menu. I've been putting Pemaquids on the menu ever since. Name is everything.

"My customers at the Oyster Bar like large oysters. I hardly have any petites on my menu, except maybe Kumamoto and Shigoku oysters, from the West Coast. They come in small, but with a deep cup. But in general, almost all my East Coast oysters are solid three-inch oysters. Size matters to my customers."

I asked him what customers tended to drink with their oysters. He replied: "The drinks that go well with oysters -- Sauvignon Blanc, Chablis, champagne and stout beer."

Sandy thinks that Maine oysters still need more name recognition. "I would recommend getting more press in The New York Times because everybody reads that."

"We go from soup to nuts as far as what people like. For me personally, I always taste the oyster naked when I first try it. That's what I tell people. Have your first oyster, nothing on it. I would say that way you can actually taste the profile and texture of the oyster. I like to chew them because I think you get a better profile and then you can put anything else you want on it. And people do, I mean, you take off from soup to nuts -- from, say, straight horseradish cocktail sauce to mignonette sauce. Not just lemon, a combination of everything."

EPILOGUE

So oyster aquaculture has great promise for the Maine Coast, and for some other coasts, too, as an expanding source of delicious nutrition and long-term economic development and as an evolving way to address some daunting environmental threats.

Oyster farmers' adaptability, so notable in this book, showed its strength as some farmers rapidly diversified their distribution to address the challenge of COVID-19, which forced the closure of much of the restaurant sector, by far the biggest buyer of oysters. Now, for example, some oyster farmers for the first time are delivering their shellfish to people at home and other non-restaurant buyers and collaborating with land farms.

But a big question is to what extent the man-made obstacles cited in this book will prevent the sector from reaching its full potential.

In any case, as the stories in this book show, Maine oyster farmers have the grit and ingenuity to press on with their work, whatever nature and man throw at them. And in doing so, they'll continue to be models of visionary and remarkably self-reliant entrepreneurialism and practical environmentalism.

Let's hope that others in the private sector, and in government, come to a greater appreciation of the potential of oyster aquaculture in the years ahead.

Opposite: Postcard of Damariscotta & Newcastle, Maine (Wikimedia)

CHRONOLOGY OF MODERN OYSTERS IN MAINE

1949: The state Department of Sea and Shore Fisheries (predecessor to the Maine Department of Marine Resources) begins efforts to reestablish oysters in Maine. Initially, fisheries managers focus on European or "flat" oysters, *Ostrea edulis*, because of their market potential. The state imports them from The Netherlands, screens them for disease and parasites, and plants them in Basin Cove, Harpswell, Boothbay Harbor and the Taunton River in Franklin. More were introduced to additional Mid Coast locations in 1954.

1963: Massive oyster kills in the Mid-Atlantic states, first in the Delaware Bay and two years later in the Chesapeake Bay. *Crassostrea virginica*, the native American or East Coast oyster, is virtually wiped out by a disease called MSX and by pollution.

1964-1967: Herb Hidu spends three years at Rutgers as a Ph.D. candidate, working with Dr. Harold Haskin to produce disease-resistant oyster stock in a hatchery in Cape May, N.J. The strategy was to compare progeny from oysters that survived the MSX kills with those from unexposed populations to see if the researchers could produce oysters that showed increased resistance.

1965: The Darling Marine Center, in Walpole, is established after industrialist Ira Darling donated his estate on the Damariscotta River to the University of Maine for establishing a marine laboratory.

1970: David Dean, then director of Darling, writes a report, "Culture of Resources in a Cold-Water Marine Environment," as part of a federal Sea Grant application. Dean's proposal features developing new culture techniques for American and European oysters, scallops and the blue mussels. Based on the proposal, the University of Maine enters the federal Sea Grant Program.

1970: David Dean hires Dr. Herb Hidu to work at Darling to help develop shellfisheries.

1970: The Maine Aquaculture Law was passed. That lets individuals for the first time lease suitable areas to raise their own private crops of shellfish, finfish and marine plants. Maine, of course, has had a rich public-fishery history, but little aquaculture. Dana Wallace, a biologist for the Maine Department of Marine Resources, is a key person.

1972: Sam Chapman joins Herb Hidu to manage the Sea Lab at the Darling Marine Center.

1972: Herb Hidu begins investigating the cultivation of oysters in Maine waters, along with Ed Myers and other entrepreneurs. With funding provided by Sea Grant, Hidu develops methods to culture the European oyster in the Damariscotta next to Darling. Experiments are successful, until the parasite *Bonamia* arrives in the mid 1980s and wipes out almost all the European oysters.

1973: First aquaculture lease in Maine is issued to Ed Myers, for mussel bottom-culture.

1976: The Maine Aquaculture Association is formed.

1976: Robert Packie writes the report "The Suitability of Maine Waters for Culturing American and European Oysters".

1977: Dick Clime and Gil Jaeger form Dodge Cove Marine Farm, on the Damariscotta.

1980: Development of Maine Aquaculture Plan by the State Planning Office.

1985: Bill Mook founds Mook Sea Farm, with hatchery, in Walpole.

1986: Partners Carter Newell, Chris Davis and Smokey McKeen found Pemaquid Oyster Company, in Damariscotta.

1987: Barbara Scully founds Glidden Point Oyster Farms.

1988: The beginning of upwellers use, partly shifting from tidal power to motor-powered upwellers.

1988: The Maine Aquaculture Training Institute, started by Pemaquid Oyster owners, establishes a 10-week training course.

1990: Official state aquaculture strategy is developed for Maine.

1990: Release of "The Aquaculture Strategy for Maine."

Early 1990's: Die-off caused by Juvenile Oyster Disease threatens American oyster farms.

Early 1990's: *Bonamia* kills off European oysters in Maine.

Late 1990's: Commercially manufactured plastic-mesh aquaculture equipment (commonly called ADPI bags) become available, replacing home-made, heavy, wood-framed equipment. The availability of mass-produced equipment that can be bought, as opposed to hand-made equipment that has to be designed and built from scratch, is a huge advance for the industry. This gear can also be easily flipped for air drying, which allows natural anti-fouling and saves much time and labor.

1999: The Maine Department of Marine Resources grants the first experimental lease for limited-purpose aquaculture (LPA). An LPA license permits the licensee to use up to 400 square feet for one calendar year for the culture of certain shellfish species and marine plants, such as kelp, using certain types of gear.

1999: Tonie Simmons founds Muscongus Bay Hatchery, in Bremen.

1999: Adam Campbell starts North Haven Oyster.

2002: Peter Horne and Dana Wallace found Flying Point Oysters.

2003: OysterGro introduces a new cage and bag system for growing oysters that drastically reduces the time and manpower required to manage and harvest oysters.

2004: Kathy Boettcher, Bruce Barber and others at UMaine determine the cause of Juvenile Oyster Disease/Rosiovarius Oyster Disease.

2004: The University of Maine receives full National Sea Grant college status.

2008: Dick Clime and Gil Jaeger sell Dodge Cove Marine Farm to Tonie Simmons

2009: The University of Maine creates the Aquaculture Research Institute on Orono campus.

2009: The disease MSX hits the Damariscotta River, killing up to 90 percent of the oysters.

2009: Scientists see ocean acidification as an intensifying threat as burning fossil fuels increases carbon dioxide in the atmosphere. A third of the CO_2 emissions go into the oceans, making the water more acidic and severely damaging some growers' oyster larvae.

2012: Big Tree Hospitality opens Eventide restaurant, in Portland.

2014: Jordan Kramer founds Winnegance Oysters, in New Meadows.

2015: Abby Barrows buys Long Cove Sea Farms, on Deer Isle, from Ginnie Olson.

2016: Gulf of Maine Research Institute publishes the report, "Maine Farmed Shellfish Analysis."

2016: The Maine Oyster Company is launched with the opening of a small farm in Phippsburg before its store in Portland is opened.

2017: The Maine Oyster Trail is launched, with some 30 oyster farms.

2017: Ben Hamilton and Cameron Barney form Love Point Oysters.

2019: Maine Department of Marine Resources issues draft approval of Mere Point Oyster Company, at Maquoit Bay.

2020: Bill Mook joins Governor Mills's Climate Change Council.

ACKNOWLEDGEMENTS

The Maine Coast is known for its stunning beauty and for its tough, hard-working, ingenious and often funny people. So doing this book has been a great pleasure, made even more so by the professional obligation to frequently enjoy one of the world's most delicious foods – The Pine Tree State's oysters.

I just wish that I had the space to print all the rich stories I heard! In a way, Mainers remind me of oysters. They can be hard to open up but once you do, you find treasures – in Mainers' case pearls of wit, wisdom, charm and common sense.

There are many people I should thank for their information, insight, suggestions, good humor and patience. But I'm particularly grateful to Bill Mook, Herb Hidu, Dick Clime, Barbara Scully and Dana Morse. And then there's my editor, Robert Whitcomb, who helped me through this adventure from the start, and my art director, Clifford Tremblay, of Blue Anchor Design, who endured the many challenges of design and production and ensured that the book would be beautiful. Finally, thanks to Margo Coolidge for her outstanding proofreading, and to Jennifer Brennan of Jennifer Brennan Design for ongoing edits to the book and website design.

"Mistah, I've been doing so much with so little for so long, I can do just about anything with nothin' in no time."

—Ron, older Maine lobsterman

Cameron	Barney	Love Point Oyster
Abby	Barrows	Long Cove Oyster Farm
Hannah	Barrows	Island Institute
Pat	Burns	Georgetown Aquaculture
Abigail	Carroll	Nonesuch Oysters
Dick	Clime	Dodge Cove Marine Farm
Monique	Coombs	Maine Coastal Fishermen's Association
Chris	Davis	Pemaquid Oyster Co.
Dana	Devereaux	Mere Point Oysters
Barry	Estabrook	New York Times
Joshua	Girbus	Darling Marine Center, University of Maine
Tom	Groenig	Island Institute
Ben	Hamilton	Love Point Oysters
Muriel	Hendrix	Working Waterfront
John	Herrigel	Maine Oyster Company
Ken	Hess	Ken Hess Editorial
Herb	Hidu	Darling Marine Center, University of Maine
Eric	Horne	Flying Point Oysters
Sandy	Ingber	Grand Central Oyster
Gil	Jaeger	Dodge Cove Marine Farm
Matt	Jones	Aquaculture North America
Jordan	Kramer	Winnegance Oyster Farm
Randy	Lacovic	Darling Marine Center, University of Maine
Jesse	Leach	Bagaduce Oyster Company
Boe	Marsh	Community Shellfish

Ben	Marten	Maine Coastal Fishermen's Association
Smokey	McKeen	Pemaquid Oyster Co.
Ryan	McPherson	Glidden Point Oyster Farms
Bill	Mook	Mook Sea Farm
Dana	Morse	Maine Sea Grant
Eric	Oransky	Maine Ocean Farm
Kathleen	Parr	
George	Parr	Upstream Trucking
Andrew	Pershing	Gulf of Maine Institute of Research
Julie	Qiu	In a Half Shell
Catherine	Schmitt	Schoodic Institute
Barbara	Scully	Scully Sea Products
David	Seigal	Cull & Pistol
Chris	Sobiech	Portland Press Herald
Aaron	Turkel	Syndct
Chris	Vonderweidt	Gulf of Maine Institute of Research
Mike	Wiley	Big Tree Hospitality
		New York Times
		Portland Press Herald
		Penobscot Bay Press
		Maine Coast Harvest Films

Additional Reading

Eat Like a Fish: My Adventures as a Fisherman Turned Restorative Ocean Farmer, by Bren Smith

Unlimited Ingenuity and Industrious Entrepreneurs: Stories of Aquafarming in Maine 1998-2016, A Collection of Stories by Muriel L. Hendrix

The Essential Oyster: A Salty Appreciation of Taste and Temptation, by Rowan Jacobsen

Oysters: A Celebration in the Raw, by Jeremy Sewall and Marion Lear Swaybill

Appreciating Oysters: An Eater's Guide to Craft Oysters from Tide to Table, by Dana Deskiewicz

The Big Oyster, by Mark Kurlansky

Eventide: Recipes for Clambakes, Oysters, Lobster Rolls, and More from a Modern Maine Seafood Shack, by Arlin Smith, Andrew Taylor, Mike Wiley, and Sam Hiersteiner

Oyster: A Gastronomic History, by Drew Smith

American Seafood: Heritage, Culture & Cookery From Sea to Shining Sea, by Barton Seaver

The Oyster Companion: A Field Guide, by Patrick McMurray

Julie Qiu's Blog
https://www.inahalfshell.com/

Maine Oyster Trail
https://seagrant.umaine.edu/extension/the-oyster-trail-of-maine/